BATMAN
THE JOKER WAR

BATMAN
WRITER
JAMES TYNION IV
ARTISTS
JORGE JIMÉNEZ
GUILLEM MARCH
CARLO PAGULAYAN
DANNY MIKI
COLORIST
TOMEU MOREY

THE JOKER WAR

LETTERER
CLAYTON COWLES

COLLECTION COVER ARTISTS
JORGE JIMÉNEZ & TOMEU MOREY

BATMAN CREATED BY
BOB KANE WITH BILL FINGER

PEFC Certified

This product is from sustainably managed forests and controlled sources

PEFC/01-31-106

www.pefc.org

BATMAN VOL. 2: THE JOKER WAR

DC Comics,
2900 West Alameda Ave.,
Burbank, CA 91505.
Printed by Transcontinental Interglobe,
Beauceville, QC, Canada. 1/1/21. First Printing.
ISBN: 978-1-77950-790-7

Barnes & Noble Exclusive Edition
ISBN: 978-1-77951-195-9

Library of Congress Cataloging-in-Publication
Data is available.

Jorge Jimenez
2020

YEARS AGO.
YOU'RE THINKING ABOUT THEM, AREN'T YOU, MASTER BRUCE?
THE BODIES.
IT'S NOT THE BODIES, ALFRED...
YOU HAVEN'T BEEN SLEEPING, SIR. NOT SINCE THE CASE BEGAN.
I KNOW WHICH CRIME SCENE IMAGES YOU'VE BEEN RIFLING THROUGH, OVER AND OVER. IT'S THEIR FACES. YOU'VE SCARRED THEM INTO YOUR MIND.
THE TEST SUBJECTS AT THE CHEMICAL PLANT.
6TV
THE CAMERA OPERATOR WHO GAVE HIM WHAT HE NEEDED TO BROADCAST HIS RANSOM VIDEOS ACROSS GOTHAM.
CLARIDGE, THE DIAMOND MAGNATE...

HOW MANY HAS THIS "JOKER" FIGURE ALREADY KILLED?
TWENTY-FOUR. AND I EXPECT TO FIND MORE BODIES AT THE RESERVOIR.
AND THEN WE CAN BRING HIS NIGHTMARE TO AN END...
I'M NOT SURE THIS WILL BE THE END.
SIR?
IT'S... DIFFICULT TO PUT INTO WORDS, ALFRED.
HIS MOTIVATIONS ARE BEYOND WHAT I'VE ENCOUNTERED, NOT JUST IN GOTHAM, BUT IN ALL MY TRAINING.
IT FEELS LIKE AN OVER-SIMPLIFICATION TO CALL HIM INSANE...
I'VE SEEN MORE BODIES THAN I CAN COUNT, BUT THERE HAS ALWAYS BEEN A REASON BEHIND THE MURDERS. WHETHER IT'S A MEANS TO AN END...
OR THERE'S SOME KIND OF THRILL IN THE KILL ITSELF. A PLEASURE THEY CAN ONLY GET THIS WAY.
TO HIM, THEY'RE JUST... MEAT...
THE CITY, THIS WHOLE WORLD AND THE PEOPLE IN IT, THEY'RE ALREADY DEAD IN HIS EYES.
HE'S JUST HELPING THEM ALONG.

THERE'S SOMETHING MORE, ISN'T THERE?
THERE'S SOMETHING YOU HAVEN'T TOLD ME.
I THINK ALL OF THIS... ALL THESE KILLINGS, AND THE RESERVOIR... I THINK THEY'RE SOME KIND OF TEST, TO UNDERSTAND MY LIMITS.
I THINK HE KNOWS HE'S GOING TO LOSE, BUT HE ALREADY KNOWS HOW HE WANTS TO COME AT ME NEXT TIME...AND THE TIME AFTER THAT.
I'M THE ONLY OTHER PERSON IN THIS WORLD HE THINKS IS ALIVE, AND BECAUSE OF THAT...
I DON'T KNOW THAT THIS BATTLE WILL EVER END.
WELL, MASTER BRUCE, AT LEAST YOU WON'T BE WAGING IT ALONE.
ALFRED?
YOU DON'T THINK I'D LET YOU FIGHT A MURDEROUS NIGHTMARE CLOWN FOR THE REST OF TIME ON YOUR OWN, DID YOU?
NOW, THE ENTRANCE TO THE VIADUCT IS ON YOUR LEFT. GET READY TO RAM THROUGH THAT GATE.
IN THREE... TWO...

BWOOM
THE GOTHAM AQUEDUCT
THE PRESENT.
...REPORTS THAT WAYNE ENTERPRISES EXPERIENCED A HOSTILE TAKEOVER THIS WEEK, AND IS UNDER NEW MANAGEMENT HAVE LIT UP THE BUSINESS WORLD...
DC COMICS PRESENTS
THE JOKER WAR
PART ONE
6N
BREAKING NEWS
JAMES TYNION IV WRITER
JORGE JIMENEZ ARTIST
ICE CREAM
...WAYNE ENTERPRISES LEGAL REPRESENTATIVES HAVE OUTED A LONG-STANDING PATTERN OF EMBEZZLEMENT CONNECTED TO BRUCE WAYNE, IN HIS SUPPORT OF THE VIGILANTE KNOWN AS BATMAN...
BAAAAAAATMAN!
17 NEWS
TOMEU MOREY COLORS
CLAYTON COWLES LETTERS

...HARLAN GRAVES, NEW LEGAL COUNSEL FOR WAYNE ENTERPRISES AND ITS NEW BOARD OF DIRECTORS, HAS DEMANDED THE BATMAN HAND OVER ALL ILLEGALLY ACQUIRED TECHNOLOGY TO THE COMPANY AT ONCE...
10
BREAKING NEWS
JIMENEZ & MOREY COVER
FRANCESCO MATTINA VARIANT COVER
THERE'S NOWHERE LEFT TO RUN!
DAVE WIELGOSZ ASSOC. EDITOR
THIS CITY DOESN'T BELONG TO YOU ANYMORE!
...UNDER DIRECTIVE OF THE WAYNE ENTERPRISES LEGAL TEAM, STATELY WAYNE MANOR IN THE PALISADES WAS REPOSSESSED BY THE CITY EARLIER TONIGHT. THERE IS NO SIGN OF BRUCE WAYNE...
BEN ABERNATHY EDITOR
IT BELONGS TO HIM!
HAHAHAHAHAHAHAHAHAHAHAA!!!
...THE GOTHAM GAZETTE HAS RECEIVED A MULTI-BILLION DOLLAR CEASE AND DESIST AFTER RELEASING AN EDITORIAL CLAIMING THE JOKER IS BEHIND THE NEW COMPANY DECISIONS. THE PAPER RETRACTED THE STORY EARLIER TODAY...
NEWSLIVE
BATMAN CREATED BY BOB KANE WITH BILL FINGER

BOOOOOOM

HEY, BOSS LADY...
WE GOT ANOTHER SHELL. NO BAT-MEAT ON THE INSIDE...JUST GEARS, MICROCHIPS, AND BURNING LEATHER.
YOU KNOW WHAT? THAT'S OKAY. WE'VE JUST ABOUT FINISHED HACKING THE MAIN COMPUTER HERE AT WAYNE ENTERPRISES...

WAYNE ENTERPRISES.
TRICORNER YARDS CAMPUS.
TELL ME WHAT HE CALLED THIS PLACE, MR. FOX.
JOKER ALWAYS LOVED HIS LITTLE NAMES FOR EVERYTHING. HE SAYS BATMAN PRETENDS IT'S THE KIDS WHO NAMED THEM, BUT HE KNOWS BETTER THAN THAT.
NUH... JOKER...I WUH...WON'T HELP...
OH, COME NOW, MR. FOX. FOCUS. YOU'RE HIS CEO NOW. YOU HAVE TO TELL HIM EVERYTHING IN THAT SWEET OLD HEAD OF YOURS. LET THE TOXIN DO THE WORK. DON'T STRUGGLE.
TELL ME WHAT HE CALLS IT.
THE HEH...
HEH HEH...
THE HIBERNACULUM.
AHH...WHERE BATS BREED. THAT'S DISGUSTING.
HE'S BEEN BREEDING ALL SORTS OF LITTLE BATS, HASN'T HE?
IT'S LIKE HE KNEW WE WERE GOING TO GET OUR HANDS ON IT. HE'S GIVEN MY BOSS THE PERFECT PRESENT, AND HE DOESN'T EVEN REALIZE IT.
WHERE...
WHERE IS JOKER?
WHERE WOULD YOU GO IF YOU WERE SUDDENLY WORTH ALMOST ONE HUNDRED BILLION DOLLARS?

PARK ROW.
"YOU'D GO SHOPPING."
MONARCH THEATRE
YOU KNOW... THEY USED TO CALL THIS PART OF PARK ROW CRIME ALLEY.
YOU DON'T SAY.
OH, YES. USED TO BE YOU COULDN'T WALK DOWN THESE STREETS WITHOUT GETTING INTO SOME TROUBLE.
IF IT GOT TOO LATE, I USED TO SLEEP UP WITH ALL THE OLD REELS.
ESPECIALLY AFTER THE WAYNES.
THAT MUST HAVE BEEN VERY HARD.
THE DAD USED TO LIKE TAKING THE SON OUT HERE, WATCH THE MOVIES HE GREW UP WITH.
THEY WERE SITTING RIGHT UP FRONT. I'D SHOW YOU, BUT I DON'T THINK I COULD FIND THE SEAT WITH MY EYES.
I USED TO SAY THAT I COULD HEAR THE SHOTS FROM IN THE PROJECTIONIST BOOTH, BUT NOW I CAN'T REMEMBER IF THAT WAS REAL OR JUST A STORY I'D TELL.
IT GETS HARDER AND HARDER TO TELL THE DIFFERENCE, DOESN'T IT?
I WAS JUST TRYING TO REMEMBER THE FIRST TIME I SAW A GOOD FRIEND OF MINE. WHEN I KNEW WE'D BE FRIENDS FOR LIFE.
I REMEMBER THE FEELING MORE THAN THE SPECIFIC MEMORY. LIKE COMING OUT OF A DREAM.
YOU KNOW... IT'S THE FUNNIEST THING... IT SOUNDS LIKE THERE ARE PEOPLE DOWN IN THE THEATER...

THIS.
YEAH... THE WIND...
PLENTY PROBABLY HAVEN'T BEEN TOUCHED IN OVER A DECADE. MAYBE LONGER.
IT'S GOING TO BE HARD TO SAY GOODBYE TO THIS PLACE...THE BOY, BRUCE WAYNE, HE CAME BY WITH A FEW OFFERS OVER THE YEARS.
BUT I THINK I'D BE CRAZY TO TURN YOU DOWN. I COULD BUY A WHOLE TOWN BACK OUT IN COAL COUNTRY WHERE MY GRANDKIDS ARE WITH THE MONEY YOU'RE OFFERING.
YOU SHOULD. MAKE YOURSELF THE MAYOR. PUT YOURSELF ON T-SHIRTS. IT'S A FUN GAME WHILE IT LASTS.
OH, NO... THAT'S NOT ME. I'M JUST GOING TO FIND SOMEWHERE QUIET.
OF COURSE I GUESS YOU'RE RICH ENOUGH YOU COULD TURN ANY PLACE INTO SOMEWHERE QUIET, COULDN'T YOU!
YEAH. THAT'S JUST WHAT I'M AFTER.
SOMEWHERE QUIET, WHERE I CAN GROW OLD. AND IT'LL ALL START HERE...
DID YOU FIND WHAT YOU WERE LOOKING FOR? DON'T KNOW WHAT KIND OF USE YOU'LL GET OUT OF THEM.
FOLKS DON'T WANT TO SEE SOMETHING THEY'VE SEEN A HUNDRED TIMES BEFORE.
THEY ALWAYS SAY THAT, BUT THEY NEVER MEAN IT. THEY WANT ALL THE PIECES IN THE RIGHT PLACES. ALL THE CHARACTERS SAYING THE PARTS THEY WANT THEM TO SAY.
WHICH ISN'T TO SAY THEY DON'T WANT SOMETHING NEW.
THEY WANT TO SEE IT PEELED BACK, TO FIND OUT THERE WAS A LAYER UNDERNEATH ALL THIS TIME THEY DIDN'T KNOW ABOUT.
ARE YOU SURE YOU DON'T HEAR THEM DOWN THERE...IN THE THEATER...
...IT SOUNDS LIKE THEY'RE LAUGHING...

KNOW WHAT? WHY DON'T WE **JOIN** THEM IN THE AUDIENCE. THE SHOW IS ABOUT TO START.
THE MARK OF ZORRO
THE SHOW?
HOW MANY SEATS DOES THIS THEATER HAVE? I WOULDN'T WANT MY FRIENDS TO RUN OUT...
YOUR FRIENDS? THE ONES LAUGHING?
I CAN SEE THEM ALL RIGHT OUT THIS TINY WINDOW...THEY'RE JUST WAITING FOR YOU. YOU AND THE REST OF THEM.
THE REST OF **WHO?**
GOTHAM.
HAHAHAHAHAHAHAH!

WAYNE ENTERPRISES.
TRICORNER YARDS CAMPUS.
COMMISSIONER BULLOCK...

BOYS, LOOK! THE DEAD **SPEAK!**
MR. GRAVES. HOW CAN THE GCPD BE OF SERVICE TO YOU TONIGHT?
YOU ARE AS CHARMING AS EVER.

I'VE JUST COME FROM FILING A **CIVIL RIGHTS INJUNCTION** TO STOP THE POLICE **HARASSMENT** OF WAYNE ENTERPRISES AND ITS OWNERS.
THE MAYOR IS ON TELEVISION RIGHT NOW INSISTING THAT YOU **DISPERSE** THE BARRICADE SURROUNDING WAYNE ENTERPRISES. HE SAYS YOU ARE LIKELY TO BE REPLACED IN THE COMING DAYS.
MY **CLIENT--**

--IS **THE JOKER.**
YOU CAN GUM UP CITY HALL AND THE COURTS ALL YOU WANT, BUT THE BOYS AND I OUT HERE KNOW THE **TRUTH.** WE KNOW WHO THE GOOD GUYS ARE AND WHO THE BAD GUYS ARE.
YOUR CLIENT **STOLE** THAT COMPANY. YOUR CLIENT IS A **MASS-MURDERING** PIECE OF **GARBAGE.** A STAIN THAT NEEDS TO GET WIPED OFF THIS CITY AND THIS WORLD.

YOU CAN TAKE THAT INJUNCTION AND SHOVE IT RIGHT UP YOUR ASS.

OFFICERS, I WOULD REMIND YOU WHO BOUGHT THAT NEW HEADQUARTERS, AND ALL YOUR NEW EQUIPMENT. IT WOULD BE A SHAME TO TAKE IT ALL AWAY.
THAT WAS **BRUCE WAYNE.**
HARVEY, YOU'RE **LOSING** THIS ONE.
WE'RE **ALL** LOSING, WHITAKER.

KEEP THE CAR RUNNING. WE'LL NEED TO PAY THE MAYOR ANOTHER VISIT TO ENSURE HE'S NOT GETTING COLD FEET.
YES SIR.

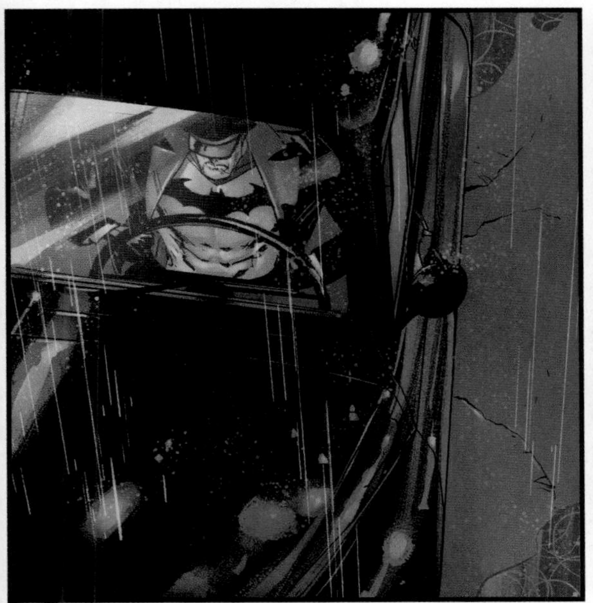

MR. UNDERBROKER...THE FOLKS IN THE WAYNE ACCOUNTING DEPARTMENT ARE GETTING SQUEAMISH. I THINK ONE OF THEM TRIED GETTING OUT A WINDOW.
I BELIEVE THAT'S WHAT THE GUNS ARE FOR, GENTLEMEN. NOW PLEASE...

GIVE ME THE LATEST ON OUR *CLIENT'S INVESTMENTS.*

AND I HAVE AN ADDED REQUEST. OUR CLIENT WISHES TO PURCHASE *EVERY* MOVIE THEATER CHAIN IN THE CITY.
NOT JUST THE *MAJORS.* THE *REVIVAL HOUSES* AND THE *ART HOUSE* INDIES IN BURNSIDE.

COST IS NO CONCERN TO HIM, BUT LET'S TRY NOT TO GIVE IT ALL AWAY, SHALL WE?
FZZZT

COMPUTER, GIVE ME EYES IN THE BUILDING. I WANT JOKER.
HE'S NOT HERE RIGHT NOW.
KRAK
OH, SORRY. WAS THIS SUPPOSED TO BE A SECRET HIDEOUT?
YOUR FRIEND MR. FOX OUTLINED THE SIX MICRO-CAVES YOU SNUCK INTO THE BUILDING.
I'M SORRY... BATMAN...
IT'S LIKE YOU PLANNED FOR EVERY TYPE OF ATTACK ON GOTHAM CITY, AND HAD A DIFFERENT CRISIS CAVE TO OPERATE OUT OF IN EACH ONE...
THIS ONE WAS MY FAVORITE. WANNA KNOW WHY?

THIS IS THE ONE YOU HADN'T EARNED YET. IT'S THE ONE THAT YOU WERE GOING TO UNLOCK WHEN YOU AND MR. FOX AND MR. WAYNE HAD FINISHED BUILDING YOUR NEW GOTHAM CITY.
KLIK
IT'S SO HOPEFUL, ISN'T IT? I LOVE THE COLOR IN THE CAPE AND COWL. IT'S NOT A DARK KNIGHT AT ALL!

I... I HADN'T SEEN...LUCIUS, YOU DESIGNED THIS?
NO... FOUND IT ON THE COMPUTER... I THOUGHT IT WAS YOU...
HAHAHAHAH! AND YOU CALL US CRAZY.
BUT YOU DON'T GET YOUR BEAUTIFUL CITY OF THE FUTURE, YOU DON'T GET YOUR NEW TOYS, AND YOU DON'T GET YOUR COOL NEW DUDS.
WE TOOK IT ALL AND NOW WE'RE GOING TO KILL YOU WITH IT.
I DON'T UNDERSTAND...
LOOKING PRETTY ROUGH OVER THERE, BATMAN. I HEARD DEATHSTROKE GOT YOU PRETTY BAD. MAYBE YOU DIDN'T GET STITCHED UP RIGHT...
OH WAIT. I KNOW WHAT IT IS...EASY TO SLIP MY MIND, SINCE I'VE SPENT THE LAST YEAR BUILDING UP MY IMMUNITIES...

WHAT'S... HAPPENING TO ME?
I FILLED YOUR LITTLE CAVE WITH POISON. IT'S MY OWN BLEND.
SOME OF THE BOSS'S STUFF, TWEAKED WITH A BIT OF FEAR TOXIN, AND A LITTLE BIT OF VENOM SO IT DOESN'T KILL YOU. MAKES THE WITHDRAWAL A HELL OF A THING, THOUGH.

NEED TO GET OUT... NEED TO GET OUT...
MASTER BRUCE... NOT THAT WAY... YOU'RE GOING BACKWARDS!
ALFRED?!

HE'S TAKEN IT ALL! YOUR VEHICLES, YOUR CITY!
MASTER BRUCE, YOU NEED TO GET OUT OF THERE!
NO...THIS ISN'T REAL! YOU'RE DEAD! YOU'RE DEAD!
I'M SORRY, MY BOY! I'M SO SORRY!

WE'RE ALL DEAD NOW.

GOTHAM CITY.
YEARS FROM NOW.
"SIR. WE'VE LOCATED THE VEHICLE. OUR DRONES ARE MAPPING THE POTENTIAL ROUTES. NINETY PERCENT HAVE THEM TAKING ADAMS."
"BIKE IS REROUTING. I'M NEARLY OVER THE NEW TRIGATE. RUN TRAFFIC PROTOCOLS TO CLEAR MY WAY, AND ALERT THE COMMISSIONER'S OFFICE."
"THERE'S A YOUNG MAN ENTERING THE MAPPED COLLISION ZONE."
"SEND UP THE SIGNAL. NO ONE DIES TODAY.
"NO ONE DIES IN THIS CITY EVER AGAIN."
Dding
HUH?
Please, step back.
WHOA... I GOT A BAT-SIGNAL... BUT THAT MEANS...

MR. FREEZE
UWOOOOM
HAHAHAH! YEAH!
IT'S BATMAN!
VICTOR. I'M JAMMING ALL RADIO FREQUENCIES. I KNOW YOU CAN HEAR ME. IF YOU SURRENDER NOW, NOBODY NEEDS TO GET HURT.

YOU CAN PUT UP THE HEAT ALL YOU WANT, BATMAN. MY SONS AND I CANNOT FEEL IT.

MY HEIRS WERE SIRED IN A DARKER, COLDER GOTHAM. WE REMEMBER THE ENDLESS NIGHTS, THE CRIME AND HORROR.
WE WILL TEAR DOWN THIS FALSE UTOPIA, AND REPLACE IT WITH SOMETHING FAR MORE CHILLING.
DAD, AT WHAT TEMPERATURE DOES THE HUMAN BRAIN FREEZE? I WOULD LIKE TO RUN AN EXPERIMENT.
IT DOESN'T MATTER, SNO-CONE. DAD'S NEW GUNS' HOTTEST TEMPS ARE STILL SUBZERO. LET'S REMIND HIM WHAT FAMILY HE'S DEALING WITH.
CHILL OUT, BATS!

SIR. ACTIVATING THE HEAT ARRAY. THE ICE DENSITY SHOULD ALLOW AN ESCAPE IN THREE, TWO...

ICEPOP! SNO-CONE! GET BEHIND ME...I CAN TAKE THE BAT.
NO, VICTOR. YOU CAN'T.
GENERATING HEATARANGS.
KZZZATTT
KZZZATTT
MY BOYS!
ARE GOING TO BE FINE. AND SO WILL YOU, VICTOR.
I PROMISE.

THAT'S THE FIRST TIME YOU'VE HAD TO GO OUT ALL MONTH. THAT HAS TO BE A RECORD, MASTER BRUCE.

I NEED TO MEET WITH **BARBARA** TO DISCUSS HOW FRIES GOT ACCESS TO HIS OLD TECHNOLOGY. AND THOSE BOYS WHO CALL THEMSELVES HIS CHILDREN...
THEY'LL NEED HELP. I CALLED **LESLIE** ON THE WAY IN. SHE AND **HARPER** WILL CHECK IN ON THEM IN THE MORNING.

YOU HAD ME WORRIED A MOMENT THERE, SIR. THAT YOU AND MRS. WAYNE WOULDN'T BE GOING ON THAT TRIP TO TOKYO AFTER ALL.
SELINA WOULD KILL ME. AND ANYWAYS...THE CITY IS WELL IN HAND.
YOUR LITTLE GOTHAM.

IT'S NOT SO LITTLE WHEN YOU'RE RACING THROUGH AT ***ONE HUNDRED MILES PER HOUR.***
ANY SURPRISES UP THERE, ALFRED?

YOUNG MASTER TIMOTHY BROUGHT CONNER WITH HIM TO DINNER. THEY HAVE A ***PROPOSAL*** OF THEIR OWN.
A VERY EXPENSIVE PROPOSAL, I'M SURE.
I'M STILL PAYING OFF THE LAST TITANS TOWER...

I CAN HEAR IN YOUR VOICE HOW MUCH YOU LOVE THE SOUND OF THESE WORDS AS THEY CROSS YOUR LIPS...

SNAP
BUT YOU KNOW THEY'RE ALL LIES.
YOUUU DON'T GET A HAPPY ENDING, BRUCE...
YOU DIE ALONE. WITH NO FAMILY. WITH NO LOVE.
AS THE CITY FALLS INTO HIS HANDS! HAHAHAAHAHA...
HAHA HAHAHAHA HAAH!
NO!
NOOOO!

GOTHAM. NOW.
NO!
HEY! YOU'RE NOT DEAD! THAT'S GOOD!
I WAS BETTING WITH MYSELF THAT YOU WERE PROBABLY DEAD.
HARLEY?
CATWOMAN... SAID YOU WERE HURT...
OH, I GOT HURT A BUNCH. BUT I KNOW PEOPLE. KNIFELINE OR WHATEVER HER NAME IS TRIED TO SHUT ME UP, BUT THIS MOUTH DON'T SHUT EASY.
A LITTLE FRANKENSTEIN, I KNOW.
I FIGURE I SHOULD LEAN IN. MAYBE MAKE IT A WHOLE HALLOWEEN THING. PAINT MYSELF GREEN.
WHERE IS THE CAT LADY ANY WAYS?
HOW LONG HAVE I BEEN OUT...?
THREE DAYS SINCE I FOUND YOU. SINCE THEY SAID YOU BLEW UP PART OF WAYNE ENTERPRISES.
FOLKS ARE PRETTY MAD ABOUT IT. BUT WE KNOW WHO'S REALLY CALLIN' THE SHOTS UP THERE NOW.

"GOTHAM CITY IS JOKER'S TOWN NOW. HE MAKES THE RULES. WHAT HE SAYS, IT'S THE TRUTH. IT'S THE TRUTH CUZ HE'S GOT THE MONEY TO MAKE IT TRUE.
"ALL THE OTHER GANGS IN THE CITY HAVE JOINED UP, BECAUSE JOKER'S PAYING THEM GONZO BUCKS. AND HE'S GIVING THEM ALL SORTS OF TOYS.
"JOKERMOBILES. JOKERCYCLES. JOKERPLANES...
"AT NIGHT, IT'S A REAL HORROR SHOW UP THERE. REGULAR FOLKS, THEY DON'T KNOW WHAT TO DO.
"THEY'RE TAKING THINGS INTO THEIR OWN HANDS, BECAUSE THE COPS AND THE CAPES? THEY'RE NOT DOING SQUAT."

SPLURCH
...okay... one down.
headshot. nice. nice. nice.
SON... SON, ARE YOU OKAY?
no ma'am. i am not even a little bit okay.
but i'm gonna see how i feel after i *kill* a bunch of these clowns.
"IT'S BAD."

AND YOU'RE STILL DOSED ON WHATEVER THAT STABBY BROAD GASSED YOU WITH. IT'S NOT THE OLD STUFF. IT'S A NEW STRAIN.
I WAS NEVER A CHEMISTRY GAL. I WAS MORE TALK THERAPY, YOU KNOW?
WHERE IS HE, HARLEY? WHERE IS JOKER IN ALL OF THIS?
SLAM
MISS PUNCH-ABLE SEEMS TO BE RUNNING THE GANG FROM THE WAYNE BUILDING AT TRICORNER YARDS.
RUMOR IS THEY JUST BOUGHT UP ALL OF ACE CHEMICAL. I BET YOU WERE THE TEST SUBJECT FOR A MUCH LARGER BATCH OF NEW JOKER TOXIN.
THE UNDERBROKER AND HIS ARMY OF LAWYERS ARE AT CITY HALL MAKING SURE THE CITY STAYS PARALYZED, AND THE COPS STEER CLEAR OF THE ACTION.
I KNOW A JOKER PLOT...AND THEY'RE PREPPING FOR THE ENDGAME... BUT MR. J?
HE'S UP TO SOMETHING DIFFERENT.
HE'S BOUGHT UP ALL THE AD TIME IN GOTHAM. ONLINE VIDEOS, AND TV. LITERALLY EVERY SPOT. IT RUNS OVER AND OVER AND OVER AGAIN.
SEE FOR YOURSELF.

A...A THRILLING TALE OF ADVENTURE... ROMANCE...AND VENGEANCE...
A STORY OF A MAN REBORN AS A HERO...
A STORY OF THE SYMBOL HE WOULD USE TO MARK THE WORLD...
TH-THE MARK OF ZORRO... REMASTERED, AND BETTER THAN EVER. THIS IS THE GOTHAM CUT.
ONLY THREE PEOPLE SAW THE ENDING LAST TIME, AND IT CHANGED THE COURSE OF THIS CITY'S HISTORY.
WHAT HAPPENS WHEN EVERYBODY SEES THE REAL ENDING?
THE MARK OF ZORRO, NOW PLAYING BACK-TO-BACK SOLD-OUT SCREENINGS AT THE MONARCH THEATER. WIDE RELEASE IS ONLY DAYS AWAY, COMING TO EVERY MOVIE HOUSE IN GOTHAM CITY!
A MOVIE SO GOOD, SO DARING, WE'RE PAYING YOU TO COME SEE IT! $10,000 TO EVERY PERSON WHO SEES IT OPENING NIGHT!
P-PLEASE, NO.
A MOVIE SO GOOD, SO DARING WE'RE PAYING YOU TO COME SEE IT! $10,000 TO EVERY PERSON WHO SEES IT OPENING NIGHT!
(PREPARE FOR THE FINAL SHOT.)
BANG!

THE MONARCH...
"NO..."
AW, JEEZ...
NO...
MOM? DAD?

SNAP
SNAP
HAHAHAHAHA
HAHAHAHAHAHA
NO!
YOU'RE LOSING IT AGAIN!
YOU GOTTA KEEP YOUR HEAD ON STRAIGHT. IF YOU GO CRAZY, MR. J IS GONNA KILL YOU!

GET BACK!
SIR. MS. QUINN HAS A TRANQUILIZER OF SOME SORT...I DON'T KNOW THAT YOU HAVE ANYTHING IN THE BELT TO COUNTERACT IT.
NO NEED TO COUNTERACT. I NEED TO KNOW WHERE I AM.

THIS IS THE J LINE PIPE SYSTEM. YOU'RE ALREADY IN PARK ROW.
GOOD. THE MONARCH'S NOT FAR.
OH BROTHER, YOU'RE HEARING VOICES, AREN'T YOU?
ALL YOUR CIRCUITS GOT FRIED IN THE BLAST, BATS. ANYTHING IN YOUR HEAD IS JUST IN YOUR HEAD!

THWMP

GOTHAM NEEDS YOU TO GET YOUR @#$$ TOGETHER, OR WE'RE ALL GONNA DIE!

SIR, ARE YOU ALL RIGHT?
JUST A LITTLE...DIZZY. I'LL GET BACK TO THE CAVE ONCE I'VE TAKEN HIM DOWN. I'M HAVING A BIT OF A PSYCHOTIC BREAK.
JUST A BIT? THAT'S A RELIEF.
YOU'RE NOT REAL, BUT I CAN DEAL WITH THAT LATER.
YOU WOUND ME, SIR. I'M HERE TO HELP YOU. I PROMISED YOU I'D ALWAYS BE HERE TO HELP YOU.
I KNOW... I KNOW. AND I CAN'T AFFORD TO LOSE ANOTHER MINUTE. I CAN'T LOSE THIS CITY AGAIN.
SIR...
ONE MOMENT, ALFRED. I SEE A SITUATION THAT NEEDS DEALING WITH.

IT'S LIKE THIS ALL OVER, ISN'T IT? I'M GOING TO NEED TO *DEAL* WITH THAT.
BUT FIRST I NEED TO DEAL WITH *HIM.*

MONARCH
MONARCH THEATRE
THE MARK OF Zorro
IT'S LIKE... I REMEMBER IT...IT'S LIKE IT'S BRAND NEW...
NOT EVEN BRAND NEW. IT'S LIKE IT WAS THAT NIGHT.
HE'S TRYING TO GET UNDER YOUR SKIN, SIR.
IT'S WORKING, ALFRED.
I'M NOT SURE IF THE HALLUCINOGENS IN THE TOXIN ARE MAKING ME SEE THE THEATER THIS WAY, OR IF JOKER USED MY MONEY TO DO IT ALL FOR REAL.
I'M GOING TO NEED TO GET UNDER *HIS* SKIN IF I'M GOING TO SURVIVE ALL OF THIS...
THE MARK OF ZORRO

GOD, THE SMELL.
WHAT IS IT?
ROT...IT'S DEATH, ALFRED. IT SMELLS LIKE DEATH IN HERE.
GIVE ME THEIR VITALS...
THERE'S NO HEARTBEAT IN THE ROOM EXCEPT YOURS...
WHY BRING THESE CORPSES HERE...SOME LOOK LIKE THEY'VE BEEN DECAYING FOR YEARS...

THAT'S BECAUSE THEY HAVE.
JOKER.
THEY'RE FAMILY. OUR FAMILY.
THEY'RE THE PEOPLE I'VE HELPED SEE TO THE OTHER SIDE OF THE VEIL. EVERY MAN, WOMAN, AND CHILD I'VE EVER KILLED...
I'VE HAD THE CLOWNS DIGGING FOR DAYS, AND I GAVE THEM A BIT OF TECH I BORROWED FROM OUR FRIEND THE DESIGNER.
AND NOW THEY'LL BE MY ARMY. AN ARMY OF JOE CHILLS READY TO KILL THIS CITY AFTER THEY SEE THE BIG PICTURE, AND SEE THE TWIST, RIGHT AT THE END.
I'VE BEEN GIVING THEM A SNEAK PEEK.
THAT'S WHY IT'S STANDING ROOM ONLY HERE AT THE MONARCH.
THEY'VE GOT A BIT OF A BONE TO PICK WITH YOU. SEE...YOU SHOULD HAVE BEEN THERE TO SAVE THEM. BUT YOU WEREN'T.
AND YOU WON'T BE ABLE TO SAVE THE REST OF THE CITY, EITHER!

HAHAHA HAHAHA HAH!
DC COMICS PRESENTS
THE JOKER WAR
PART TWO
JAMES TYNION IV WRITER JORGE JIMENEZ ARTIST
TOMEU MOREY COLORS CLAYTON COWLES LETTERS
JIMENEZ & MOREY COVER FRANCESCO MATTINA VARIANT COVER
DAVE WIELGOSZ ASSOC. EDITOR BEN ABERNATHY EDITOR
BATMAN CREATED BY BOB KANE WITH BILL FINGER

TRICORNER YARDS.
AND THIS IS EVERYTHING?
EVERY CANISTER I ASKED FOR?
YES. I'VE CHECKED THE MANIFESTS PERSONALLY. THEY ARE ALL OURS, TOTALLY LEGITIMATELY.
TOXIC
IT'S ONLY BEEN A DAY.
WE OUTBID THE SUPPLY SHIPS EN ROUTE TO OTHER NEARBY PORTS. IN ONE CASE, I MADE THE CALL TO BUY THE SHIP OUTRIGHT.
I $#%&!?€ LOVE BEING RICH.

BOYS, WHEN THESE ARE LOADED UP, YOU'RE GOING TO BE MAKING THE TRIP DIRECTLY TO *ACE CHEMICAL.* THE BOSS WANTS THE NEW FORMULA COOKING BY THE END OF THE DAY.

IS THIS... UH...
IS THIS IT? NO *SECURITY?*

YOU'RE THE SECURITY.

I JUST MEAN...THE GUYS HAVE BEEN TALKING. WE GOTTA PASS THROUGH THE NARROWS TO GET TO ACE...
CLOWNS DON'T DO TOO HOT IN THE NARROWS RIGHT NOW.

TALK *FASTER.* MAKE ME *CARE.*
S-SORRY... TWELVE CLOWNS DEAD IN THE NARROWS, YESTERDAY.
BATS *DON'T* KILL.
THIS WASN'T A BAT. THIS WAS SOMETHING *ELSE.* SOMETHING *WEIRDER.*

THE NARROWS.
YESTERDAY.
I AM HITTING THE ACCELERATOR, REGGIE! IT'S NOT DOING A DAMN THING!
um... hi.
so, those controls don't work too good, huh?
wasn't sure if i could short-circuit one of your fancy cars. but it looks like i just needed a transformer and a fire hydrant.
THIS USED TO BE A BATMOBILE. YOU'RE NOT BREAKING IN, KID.
oh, i don't really care to break in. gonna be hot hot hot in there.
i've got my anti-clown toxin here. i bought it down at the gas station.
IS THIS... GASOLINE?!
WHO THE @$@@ DO YOU THINK YOU ARE?!

i'm clownhunter.
sorry. that sucks for you. i know.
IF YOU'RE SCARED OF THE NARROWS, GO AROUND THE NARROWS. BUT I WANT YOU TO KEEP THIS IN MIND...
THIS, RIGHT HERE? THIS IS THE KEY TO JOKER'S BIG PLAN FOR GOTHAM CITY. IT'S GOING TO HELP MAKE A WHOLE NEW BLEND OF HIS OLD TOXIN.
AND YOU NEED TO DECIDE RIGHT NOW...WHO YOU'RE REALLY AFRAID OF...
SOME KID...OR THE GUY WHO'S ABOUT TO KILL BATMAN.

MONARCH THEATRE
YOU'VE NEVER BEEN ONE TO LOOK FAILURE IN THE FACE, HAVE YOU, BATS?
WELL, HERE IT IS, READY TO TEAR YOU TO PIECES. SOME OF THESE BAGS OF BONES HAVE BEEN ROTTING IN THE DIRT FOR YEARS... SOME ARE MUCH FRESHER.
WHICH DO YOU THINK ARE ANGRIER? THE ONES WHO WERE THERE AT THE BEGINNING, WHEN I WAS A VERY DIFFERENT SORT OF CLOWN? BACK WHEN YOU UNDERESTIMATED HOW MANY CASUALTIES THERE'D BE...
OR IS IT THE RECENT DEAD...THE ONES WHO DIED WITH YOU KNOWING THAT THE LONGER I STAYED ALIVE THE MORE OF THEM WOULD GO THE WAY OF THE REAPER?
I GUESS IT DOESN'T MATTER. THEY'RE ALL ANGRY. THEY'RE ALL DISAPPOINTED...
THEY ALL WANT YOU DEAD.

NOW, ME... I THINK THEY'RE A LITTLE IMPATIENT, IF I'M BEING HONEST.
I THINK IT'LL BE BETTER IF THINGS GO ACCORDING TO MY PLAN.
KILLING YOU IS EASY. IT WON'T HURT YOU ENOUGH. BUT MAKING EVERYONE IN GOTHAM CITY RELIVE YOUR CHILDHOOD TRAUMA?
NOW THAT'S WHAT I CALL FUN!
HAHAHAHAHAHAHA!
PICTURE IT, BATS...THEY'RE ALL GOING TO COME TO WATCH MY SPECIAL CUT OF ZORRO. THEY WON'T BE ABLE TO STOP THEMSELVES. I'M OFFERING TOO MUCH MONEY!
THEY'LL FEEL JUST LIKE YOU DID THAT NIGHT IN THE THEATER... ALL THE DRAMA AND ROMANCE AND POWER OF THE OLD LEGEND.
AND AT THE END OF IT, I'LL REVEAL THE TRUTH: THAT YEARS AGO IDDLE WIDDLE BRUCE WAYNE WAS JUST LIKE THEM.
THEN THE BAD MAN CAME WITH THE GUN. AND SURVIVING THAT MADE HIM INTO BATMAN.
AND I'LL ASK THEM WHAT IT'LL TURN THEM INTO, BEFORE THE GAS STARTS FILLING THE THEATERS.
DON'T LISTEN TO HIM, MASTER BRUCE...KEEP YOUR FOCUS.
I'M TRYING, ALFRED... PUNCHLINE'S TOXIN IS STILL SO STRONG. IT'S TWISTING REALITY AROUND ME...

WHAT I'M SEEING IS IMPOSSIBLE...
JUST LISTEN TO THE SOUND OF MY VOICE. KEEP YOURSELF GROUNDED.
HH. YOU'RE NOT REAL EITHER.
I BEG YOUR PARDON--
I'M LOSING MY GRIP. HEARING HIS VOICE IS TWISTING MY MIND. I NEED HIM TO SHUT UP.
HAHAHAHAHAHA!
I'M NOT EXACTLY THE SHUTTING UP TYPE, BATMAN!
I AM THE VOICE OF GOD, THE GREAT OZ SHOUTING DOWN FROM THE BIG SCREEN. SHOUTING MY WAY INTO YOUR BRAIN. JUST LIKE I'LL DO TO THE REST OF THEM.
MAYBE SOME OF THOSE GOTHAMITES WILL GET AWAY AND COME TRY TO FIGHT ME A FEW DECADES DOWN THE ROAD, WHEN I'VE BUILT MY WHOLE NEW WORLD ON THE ASHES OF YOUR OLD ONE.
ISN'T THAT NICE TO THINK ABOUT?
00:03
00:02
NOW, THEY'LL PROBABLY HATE YOU TOO, JUST LIKE ALL OF THESE CORPSES...BECAUSE YOU WEREN'T THERE TO STOP ME.
00:01
THEY'LL KNOW THE TRUTH... THAT IT'S ALL YOUR--
00:00
beeebeebeep

I SAID SHUT UP!

OM
SIR...
THE TOXIN IS TOO MUCH. I CAN'T TRUST MY EYES.
RRRIP
BUT I DON'T NEED THEM TO FIGHT.

A GOOD BAT KNOWS HOW TO FIGHT BLIND.
WHAM
KRAK
BAM
WHAK
SLAM
SIR...SIR. THEY'RE RELENTLESS. YOU CAN'T SURVIVE THIS FOR LONG.

I DON'T NEED TO...I JUST NEEDED TO MOVE TO THE CENTER OF THE BATTLEFIELD.
ENOUGH SO THESE NANOBOT MONSTROSITIES ARE IN RANGE OF THE PORTABLE EMP.
BUT SIR. THAT'LL SHORT YOUR RADIO... YOU'LL LOSE ME...
I KNOW, ALFRED. BUT THERE'S NO CHOICE.
WMWOMWOMWOMWOMWOMWOMWOMWOMWOMWO
HH...
OKAY... STAY ON YOUR FEET...

UNNGH... ONE FOOT... AFTER...THE OTHER.

HUHHH...

EN GARDE!
HAHAH, BRUCE, BE CAREFUL. YOU'LL PUT AN EYE OUT.
I'M NOT BRUCE, I'M ZORRO!
THOMAS, ARE YOU SURE THIS SHORTCUT IS SAFE?

NO...
NO! TURN BACK!
TURN...
UNNNGH.
OH BROTHER... HERE WE GO AGAIN...

YOU KNOW, I NEVER THOUGHT I'D HAVE A TASTE FOR THE FINER THINGS.
I WAS A DIRTY LITTLE STREET CLOWN, AND IF I SAW AN UPTURNED NOSE, I JUST WANTED TO STICK A KNIFE IN IT.
BUT THE HIGH LIFE GROWS ON YOU. LIKE SOME KIND OF HORRIBLE GOLDEN FUNGUS.
IT'S BEAUTIFUL, ISN'T IT, PUNCHLINE?
FROM UP HERE THE PEOPLE LOOK LIKE LITTLE FLEAS SWARMING OVER THE ROTTING CARCASS OF GOTHAM, AND WE'RE HERE TO GAS THEM OUT.
BATMAN'S STILL OUT THERE.

THIS IS HOW IT GOES, MY SWEET. I MAKE MY MOVE, HE MAKES HIS. IT HAPPENS IN TURNS. HE'S TOO HOPPED-UP ON THAT DELIGHTFUL TOXIN OF YOURS TO MAKE A PLAY RIGHT NOW.
NOW WE GET A QUIET BEAT, WHERE WE CAN SAVOR THE ANARCHY IN THE STREETS.

I'M NOT SURE WHAT THERE IS TO SAVOR.
THERE'S SOMETHING HAPPENING IN THE NARROWS. SOME TEENAGER KEEPS KILLING OUR CLOWNS.

"ONE OF OUR MEN, BURNED HALF TO DEATH, TOLD ME THE KID'S CALLING HIMSELF CLOWNHUNTER. HE JUST TOOK OUT ONE OF OUR TRUCKS EN ROUTE TO ACE CHEMICAL."

HAHAHAHAHAHA, SEE, ISN'T THAT WONDERFUL?!

WONDERFUL?

THE VIGILANTES OF GOTHAM, THEY DON'T KILL. ALL HIS LITTLE BATS AND BIRDS. THAT'S ONE OF THE RULES OF THIS CITY.
WHENEVER ONE OF THE LITTLE ONES GETS THE STUPID IDEA TO PUT ON A MASK THEY FOLLOW HIS RULES, HIS SYMBOL.
THIS BEAUTIFUL, HORRIBLE KID KNOWS THAT THE RULE BOOK HAS BEEN THROWN OUT! HAHAHAHAHA!
SO YOU WANT TO LET HIM JUST KEEP KILLING OUR PEOPLE?
NO. SEND SOME OF OUR HEAVY HITTERS TO CRUCIFY HIM ON THE STREETS TO LET THE CITY KNOW WE WON'T TOLERATE THAT KIND OF THING. BUT IT'S A GOOD SIGN.
AND THEN I THINK IT'S TIME TO DOUSE MY FORMER FLAME.
ABOUT @$#%# TIME.
IF YOU'RE OUT TO BREAK HARLS, THERE'S ONLY ONE REAL WAY TO GET UNDER HER SKIN.

"YOU HAVE TO GO RIGHT FOR THE HEART."
MMMNNNNH...

ACE... *ACE,* IS THAT YOU?

YES, IT'S ME! ACE THE BAT-HOUND!
WHAT? WHAT THE...

HAHAHA. SORRY, BATS. WE GOTTA STOP MEETING LIKE THIS. PEOPLE WILL SAY WE'RE IN *LOVE.*

WHERE THE HELL DID YOU TAKE ME, HARLEY?
EDEN.
THAT'S WHAT *PAMMY* CALLED IT, ANYWAYS.

THIS IS IN GOTHAM?
OH, COME ON, BATS. YOU KNOW A LOT ABOUT THIS CITY, BUT YOU DON'T KNOW EVERYTHING. THERE ARE LOTS OF WEIRD WILD LITTLE CORNERS WHERE US LOONEYS GO IN BETWEEN OUR BIG CRIMES.
SHE BUILT THIS PARADISE FOR ME IN A CAVE SYSTEM UNDER THE PARK, AFTER A ROUGH TIME WITH MR. J... I WASN'T READY TO LET GO OF HIM THEN, BUT HE'D POISONED ME...
THIS WAS KINDA SORTA MY REHAB CLINIC. THAT'S WHY I WANTED TO BRING YOU HERE.
IVY'S USUAL RULES ARE NO CLOTHES IN EDEN, BUT I DON'T THINK YOU AND I HAVE THAT KIND OF RELATIONSHIP.
AND IF ANY OF THESE PLANTS HAVE HER RESIDUAL PERSONALITY, THEY'D PROBABLY TRY HARDER TO EAT YOU.
THIS IS WHERE I USED TO GO WITH HER TO GET MY BRAIN IN ORDER. TO A POINT, ANYWAYS...
I WANT YOU TO DRINK THIS.
WHAT IS IT?
IT'LL NEGATE THE EFFECTS OF THE POISON THAT'S MAKING YOU GO NUTS AND FIGHT PEOPLE BLINDFOLDED WHILE YOU TALK TO PEOPLE WHO AREN'T THERE.
FLUSH ALL THOSE BAD CHEMICALS OUT OF YOUR SYSTEM.
TRUST ME. I'M A DOCTOR.

HARLEY...
LOOK, BATS. THERE'S SOMETHING DIFFERENT ABOUT ALL OF THIS. THIS ISN'T HOW THE JOKER USUALLY MAKES AN ATTACK. LIKE HIS PRIORITIES HAVE SHIFTED.
THE MATH OF IT ALL IS SIDEWAYS. AND YOU'RE THE ONLY ONE WHO CAN CRACK IT.
BUT CRAZY BATMAN ISN'T CRACKING @#$&, SO DRINK YOUR PLANT SMOOTHIE AND DON'T GIVE ME LIP OR I'LL HIT YOU WITH A BIG HAMMER.
HARLEY, WHAT'S HAPPENING?
UNNNGH...
HARLEY...

HEY, NICE! THAT MEANS IT'S WORKING. NOW, YOU'LL BE OUT FOR A WHILE.
OUT... FOR A WHILE?
YEAH, YOU'RE GOING TO TRIP BALLS FIRST, BUT IT'LL FLUSH THE REST OF THE NASTY OUT OF YOUR SYSTEM. SEE YOU IN A BIT.
THIS ISN'T REAL... THIS ISN'T REAL.
I KNOW, MY BOY.

AND I'M VERY SORRY, MASTER BRUCE, BUT I THINK IT'S TIME WE HAD A SERIOUS TALK.

DC COMICS PRESENTS

THE JOKER WAR

PART THREE

JAMES TYNION IV WRITER JORGE JIMENEZ ARTIST
TOMEU MOREY COLORS CLAYTON COWLES LETTERS
GUILLEM MARCH & TOMEU MOREY COVER
FRANCESCO MATTINA VARIANT COVER
DAVE WIELGOSZ ASSOC. EDITOR BEN ABERNATHY EDITOR
BATMAN CREATED BY BOB KANE WITH BILL FINGER

FINCH

YOU'RE AFRAID.
I AM NOT AFRAID. I'M THINKING, CRANE.

THINKING OF ALL THE WAYS YOU'RE GOING TO FAIL.
IMAGINING THE BAT SITTING ACROSS FROM YOU. HOW WOULD HE COUNTER EACH AND EVERY ONE OF YOUR MOVES?
THAT'S NOT WHAT I'M DOING.

THAT'S WHAT YOU'RE ALWAYS DOING, RIDDLER.
YOU WANTED TO PLAY THIS GAME, SCARECROW. I DID NOT MAKE YOU PLAY.
I THINK I WAS PLAYING A DIFFERENT GAME.
IT'S CHESS. WE'RE PLAYING CHESS. DELIBERATION IS AN IMPORTANT--DARE I SAY--CRUCIAL--PART OF THE GAME.

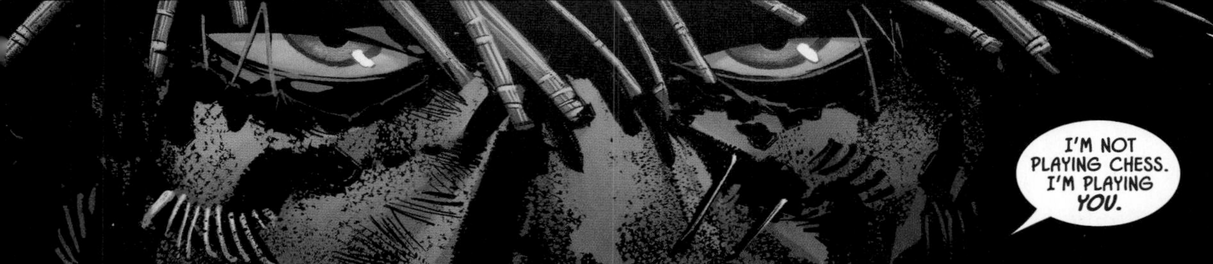
I'M NOT PLAYING CHESS. I'M PLAYING YOU.

YOU SONUVA--

WELL, THAT WAS PREDICTABLE. DID ANYONE PUT ANY MONEY DOWN ON HOW QUICKLY EDDIE WOULD FLIP THE BOARD?
NO? PITY. I HATE LEAVING EASY MONEY ON THE TABLE.
AH, MS. KYLE. I SEE YOU'VE GRACED US WITH YOUR PRESENCE. YOU'RE HEALING NICELY.
NOW, WE'VE MADE A BIT OF A GAME OF IT, WITH EDDIE'S HELP. A KIND OF BINGO BOARD WHERE YOU PLACE YOUR BETS ON THE LATEST FIRES JOKER'S HENCHMEN SET IN THE CITY.
FIREFLY IS DOING REMARKABLY WELL. I THINK I MIGHT HIRE HIM FOR A FEW JOBS WHEN THIS IS DONE.
THIS IS ALL MY FAULT. I GAVE HIM THE WEAPON HE NEEDED TO DO THIS.
I GAVE HIM THE MONEY TO FUND HIS WAR, PENGUIN.
DON'T UNDERSELL YOURSELF, DEAR.
YOU GAVE HIM THE MONEY TO WIN HIS WAR.
IS...HAS THERE BEEN ANY SIGN OF HIM? OF BATMAN?
NO. THE BAT APPEARS TO HAVE BEEN TAKEN OFF THE BOARD.
COME ON NOW, BAT. PULL YOURSELF TOGETHER. THE CITY'S IN PAIN. IT'S CALLING OUT TO YOU.

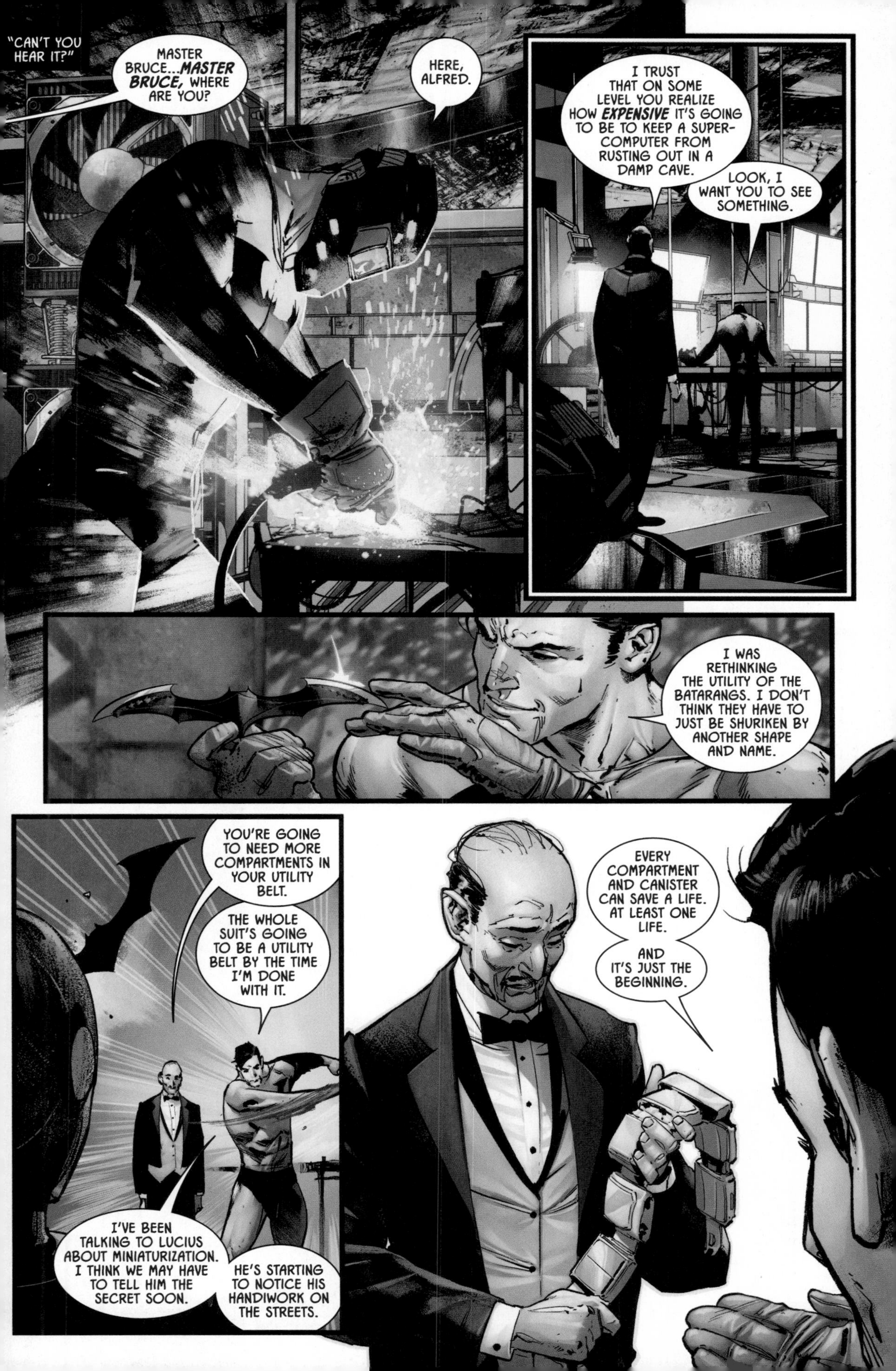
"CAN'T YOU HEAR IT?"
MASTER BRUCE...MASTER BRUCE, WHERE ARE YOU?
HERE, ALFRED.
I TRUST THAT ON SOME LEVEL YOU REALIZE HOW EXPENSIVE IT'S GOING TO BE TO KEEP A SUPER-COMPUTER FROM RUSTING OUT IN A DAMP CAVE.
LOOK, I WANT YOU TO SEE SOMETHING.
I WAS RETHINKING THE UTILITY OF THE BATARANGS. I DON'T THINK THEY HAVE TO JUST BE SHURIKEN BY ANOTHER SHAPE AND NAME.
YOU'RE GOING TO NEED MORE COMPARTMENTS IN YOUR UTILITY BELT.
THE WHOLE SUIT'S GOING TO BE A UTILITY BELT BY THE TIME I'M DONE WITH IT.
I'VE BEEN TALKING TO LUCIUS ABOUT MINIATURIZATION. I THINK WE MAY HAVE TO TELL HIM THE SECRET SOON.
HE'S STARTING TO NOTICE HIS HANDIWORK ON THE STREETS.
EVERY COMPARTMENT AND CANISTER CAN SAVE A LIFE. AT LEAST ONE LIFE.
AND IT'S JUST THE BEGINNING.

THERE'S PART OF YOU THAT STILL THINKS IT'S POSSIBLE, EVEN NOW...
YOUR BRAIN IS REACHING INTO YOUR MEMORIES TO FIND THE RIGHT KIND OF OPTIMISM. YOU WANT DESPERATELY TO BE THIS VERSION OF YOURSELF.
ALFRED?

I... I DON'T UNDERSTAND WHAT YOU MEAN.
OF COURSE YOU DO, MASTER BRUCE. YOU HAVE THE KEENEST MIND OF ANY MAN I'VE KNOWN.

HARLEY QUINN... GAVE ME SOME TEA.
YES.
YOU'RE NOT REAL. YOU'RE DEAD.
YES.
ALFRED...

BUT YOU AREN'T.
YOU'VE BEEN GIVEN THE GIFT OF BEING ABLE TO STEP BACK FROM THE ACTION TO TAKE AN AERIAL VIEW. TO SEE THE BIG PICTURE YOU HAVEN'T LET YOURSELF SEE.
YOU HAVE NO IDEA HOW LONG IT WILL TAKE FOR MS. QUINN'S CONCOCTION TO PURGE THE TOXINS FROM YOUR SYSTEM.

NOW, IF WE'RE GOING TO HAVE SOME TEA, LET'S DO IT PROPERLY.

TEA... SOUNDS NICE...
HELL NO. YOU'VE HAD ENOUGH TEA.
YOU'RE PROBABLY SEEIN' A WHOLE SINGIN' AND DANCIN' NUMBER RIGHT NOW. BATMAN: THE MUSICAL ON ICE. EVERYONE WITH THOSE BIG FOAM HEADS.
IVY, IF YOU'RE LISTENING THROUGH YOUR PLANTS, THIS WOULD BE A REAL GOOD TIME TO SHOW UP AND TELL ME WHETHER I GOT THE DOSES RIGHT.
I NEED POINTY EARS OVER HERE TO GET HIS @$$@ TOGETHER.
JUST A NICE QUICK DAY TRIP, NOT A FULL WEEKEND AT WOODSTOCK.
THE KITCHEN...
AND NOW HE'S GOT THE MUNCHIES. GOD HELP US.
DO YOU EVER SHUT UP?
I REALLY SHOULD HAVE CUT JUST A LITTLE DEEPER...
PAMMY? IS THAT YOU?

AW...YOU THOUGHT IF YOU BROUGHT BATMAN HERE YOU COULD LURE YOUR OLD GIRLFRIEND OUT OF HIDING? THAT'S SWEET.
BUT HARLEY, YOU REALLY SHOULD HAVE PICKED SOMEWHERE A WHOLE LOT LESS FLAMMABLE.
PUNCHING BAG! ER... I MEANT... PUNCHLINE!
DC COMICS PRESENTS
THE JOKER WAR
PART FOUR
JAMES TYNION IV WRITER JORGE JIMENEZ ARTIST
TOMEU MOREY COLORS CLAYTON COWLES LETTERS
GUILLEM MARCH & TOMEU MOREY COVER
FRANCESCO MATTINA VARIANT COVER
DAVE WIELGOSZ ASSOC. EDITOR BEN ABERNATHY EDITOR
BATMAN CREATED BY BOB KANE WITH BILL FINGER

TELL ME WHAT YOU SEE, MASTER BRUCE. WHICH TEA AM I POURING FOR YOU?
IT'S YOUR DARJEELING BLEND. THE ONE FROM THE CUPBOARD TO THE LEFT OF THE PANTRY.
YOU KEEP IT IN A GLASS JAR. YOU WOULD BRING IT TO ME IN THE CAVE ON THE CASES WHERE I WAS MOST DISTURBED AND FRIGHTENED.
YOU THOUGHT I DIDN'T NOTICE. IT WAS YOUR WAY OF TELLING ME YOU KNEW I WAS AFRAID, BUT THAT I WOULDN'T SAY IT OUT LOUD, AND YOU WERE TELLING ME IT WOULD ALL BE OKAY.
I TRIED MAKING IT THE MONTH AFTER YOU PASSED, BUT IT DIDN'T TASTE THE SAME.
IF ONLY YOU'D STUDIED UNDER THE GREAT TEA MASTERS OF CHINA IN YOUR TRAVELS.
IF ONLY.
TELL ME HOW BAD IT IS.
HE'S USING MY FAMILY'S MONEY TO TIE UP THE LEGAL SYSTEM TO KEEP HIS GANGS ON THE STREETS, TERRORIZING PEOPLE. KILLING PEOPLE.
HE'S TAKEN THE FORTUNE. THE MANOR. WAYNE ENTERPRISES. HE HAD LUCIUS POISONED AND FORCED HIM TO HELP MODIFY MY VEHICLES INTO SOMETHING DEADLY.
HE'S GOING TO KILL *THOUSANDS* MORE AFTER MAKING THEM WATCH THE SAME MOVIE I WATCHED THE NIGHT I LOST MY PARENTS.
GOTHAM CITY'S DEATH BOUGHT AND PAID FOR BY THE *WAYNE FORTUNE.*

YOU SAW IT FROM THE BEGINNING.
THE JOKER LIVES IN A COLD, DEAD WORLD, WHERE YOU AND HE ARE THE ONLY REAL LIVING BEINGS.
HE MOCKS LOVE AND FAMILY BY PULLING HIS ACOLYTES CLOSE TO HIM. MAKING A JOKE OF YOUR FAMILY. YOUR RELATIONSHIPS.
BUT HE'D JUST AS SOON PUT A BULLET IN THEIR HEADS IF THAT GAVE HIM THE UPPER HAND AGAINST YOU.
HE PUTS SO MANY LIVES AT RISK SO YOU KNOW YOU CAN'T SAVE THEM ALL.
BECAUSE HE KNOWS YOU ARE HIS OPPOSITE.
THERE IS NO DIFFERENCE TO HIM IN TAKING ONE LIFE OR A MILLION LIVES.
BUT THERE IS TO YOU.

FWOOSH
OH, COME ON, HARLEY. I THOUGHT YOU LIKED TO HAVE A LITTLE FUN.
WHY ARE YOU SO DAMN HEAVY?! YOU JUMP OFF ROOFS, FOR GOD'S SAKE.
THIS WOULD BE A REALLY #$%#@ GOOD TIME TO WAKE UP, BY THE WAY.
BATMAN'S NOT GOING TO SAVE YOU, YOU OLD CLOWN. HE'S NOT SAVING ANYONE.
THAT TOXIN RUNNING THROUGH HIS SYSTEM WILL TAKE DAYS OF AGONY TO CLEAR. AND BY THEN THERE WON'T EVEN BE A CITY LEFT TO SAVE.
STOP HIDING BEHIND YOUR FAILED HERO.
YEAH, OKAY. I'LL HIDE BEHIND THIS BIG FREAKING GUN INSTEAD.

BLAM
YOU KNOW, PUNCHY, I'M REALLY STARTING TO NOT LIKE YOU VERY MUCH.
TRYING TO CUT MY THROAT OPEN WAS ONE THING, BUT THEN YOU COME TO BURN DOWN THE ONLY PLACE I STILL LIKE IN THIS STUPID CITY?
I DON'T KNOW HOW JOKER TWISTED YOU UP LIKE THIS--
YOU DON'T KNOW ANYTHING.
YOU NEVER HAVE. AND I SURE AS HELL DON'T NEED A FLAMETHROWER TO KILL YOU.
OH, HONEY. I WENT SOFT ON YOU LAST TIME.
THIS TIME AROUND I'M NOT GOING TO HOLD BACK...

YOU THINK YOU'RE SOMEBODY BECAUSE YOU HAD SOME KIND OF IDIOTIC COME-TO-GOD MOMENT AFTER YOU LOST THE JOKER?
SOMEBODY'S BOUGHT INTO THEIR OWN HYPE.
YOU DON'T KNOW WHAT YER TALKIN' ABOUT, KID.
OF COURSE I DO!
EVERYONE KNOWS HOW PATHETIC HARLEY QUINN IS!
"THE BRILLIANT YOUNG GRADUATE STUDENT WHO GOT A GIG AT ARKHAM TO WRITE HER DISSERTATION ON THE BADDEST OF THE BAD.
THESIS
A+
"WHERE SHE MEETS THE JOKER.
"AND FINDS OUT THAT UNDERNEATH ALL THAT LIPSTICK AND HORROR IS A SENSITIVE GUY, AND IF ONLY THAT ROTTEN BATMAN GOT OUT OF THE WAY, THEY COULD BE HAPPY TOGETHER.
"SO SHE BUSTS HIM OUT AND BECOMES HIS MAIN SQUEEZE..."

...BECAUSE SHE'S TOO #$%$ STUPID TO REALIZE SHE WAS JUST A MEANS TO AN END.
AND WHAT THE HELL DO YOU THINK YOU ARE?
I WAS IN SCHOOL WHEN I SAW THAT THE WORLD WAS FALLING APART AROUND ME, AND EVERYONE WAS PRETENDING IT WASN'T.
"I FELT LIKE I WAS GOING CRAZY.
"UNTIL I HEARD HIM SPEAK.
"IT TOOK ME A YEAR TO FIND HIM, OUT IN THE WORLD. TO JOIN HIS CAUSE AND TAKE DOWN THIS FAKE SOCIETY.
"IT TOOK LONGER TO PROVE TO HIM THAT I WAS SERIOUS.*
*TO SEE THE ORIGIN OF PUNCHLINE, SEE THE JOKER 80TH ANNIVERSARY SPECIAL, ON SALE NOW! --BEN
"I BELIEVE IN THE JOKER. IN WHAT HE STANDS FOR.
"AND I'LL BE AT HIS SIDE WHEN HE FINALLY KILLS BATMAN, AND WE TAKE THIS WAR FROM CITY TO CITY, UNTIL EVERYONE HAS HEARD HIS MESSAGE."

Y'KNOW? I FEEL SORRY FOR YOU, KID. YOU STILL DON'T SEE THAT WE'RE EXACTLY THE SAME.
I THOUGHT MR. J HAD A HEART. YOU THINK HE HAS A BRAIN.
BUT HE'S NOT DOING THIS FOR ANY OF THE REASONS YOU THINK HE IS. HE DOESN'T BELIEVE IN ANYTHING.
HE'S A MANIPULATOR. HE'S MANIPULATING YOU.
YOU DON'T GET IT. YOU WANT EVERYONE TO BE AS STUPID AS YOU WERE.
WHAM
WSSH
KRAK

I FEEL SORRY FOR YOU, PUNCHY. BUT NOT SORRY ENOUGH TO NOT KICK YOUR ASS.
THERE'S NOTHING IN THIS WORLD HE'S EVER GOING TO CARE ABOUT MORE THAN THAT STUPID BAT.
THWAK
YOU'RE WRONG.
AND I'LL PROVE IT.
I'LL SHOW YOU WHAT JOKER REALLY BELIEVES ONCE I KILL BATMAN MYSELF.

YOU TAKE YOURSELF SO SERIOUSLY, MASTER BRUCE. BUT BATMAN IS A CHILD'S DREAM. THAT YOU CAN TRAVEL THE WORLD AND LEARN EVERY POSSIBLE WAY TO SAVE EVERYONE.
AND THERE IS A PART OF YOU THAT BELIEVES YOU CAN.
AND THAT DREAM IS POWERFUL, AND BEAUTIFUL, AND YOU MUST HOLD ONTO IT.
BUT THERE IS A WEIGHT TO THE PROMISE YOU MADE TO YOURSELF AS A BOY. IT WOULD CRUSH ANY OTHER MAN. AND IT HAS NEARLY CRUSHED YOU MORE TIMES THAN I CAN COUNT.
AND SINCE YOU LOST ME... IT'S COME THE CLOSEST I'VE SEEN.
I'M SORRY.
NO, BOY. LISTEN TO ME. LOOK ME IN THE EYES.

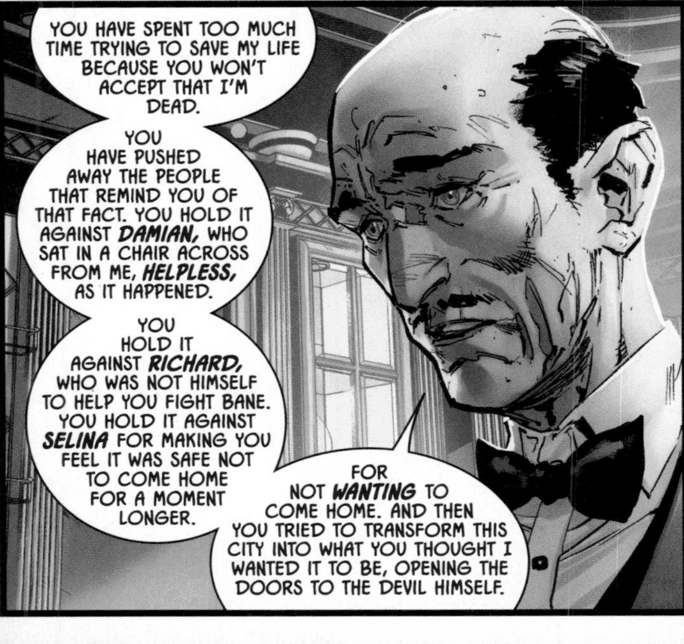
YOU HAVE SPENT TOO MUCH TIME TRYING TO SAVE MY LIFE BECAUSE YOU WON'T ACCEPT THAT I'M DEAD.
YOU HAVE PUSHED AWAY THE PEOPLE THAT REMIND YOU OF THAT FACT. YOU HOLD IT AGAINST DAMIAN, WHO SAT IN A CHAIR ACROSS FROM ME, HELPLESS, AS IT HAPPENED.
YOU HOLD IT AGAINST RICHARD, WHO WAS NOT HIMSELF TO HELP YOU FIGHT BANE. YOU HOLD IT AGAINST SELINA FOR MAKING YOU FEEL IT WAS SAFE NOT TO COME HOME FOR A MOMENT LONGER.
FOR NOT WANTING TO COME HOME. AND THEN YOU TRIED TO TRANSFORM THIS CITY INTO WHAT YOU THOUGHT I WANTED IT TO BE, OPENING THE DOORS TO THE DEVIL HIMSELF.

I FAILED.

SLAP
NO. NO, DAMMIT!
THIS STORY ISN'T OVER YET.
YOU ARE BATMAN.
YOU NEED TO ACCEPT THE WORLD YOU LIVE IN AND ACCEPT WHAT YOU CAN CONTROL.

YOU NEED TO ACCEPT THAT YOU DID NOT AND CANNOT SAVE ME.
YOU ALSO NEED TO ACCEPT THAT YOU DID NOT AND CANNOT SAVE YOUR PARENTS.

BUT YOU CAN SAVE YOURSELF.
AND IN DOING SO, YOU CAN SAVE THE LIVES OF SO MANY PEOPLE IN THAT CITY YOU LOVE SO MUCH.

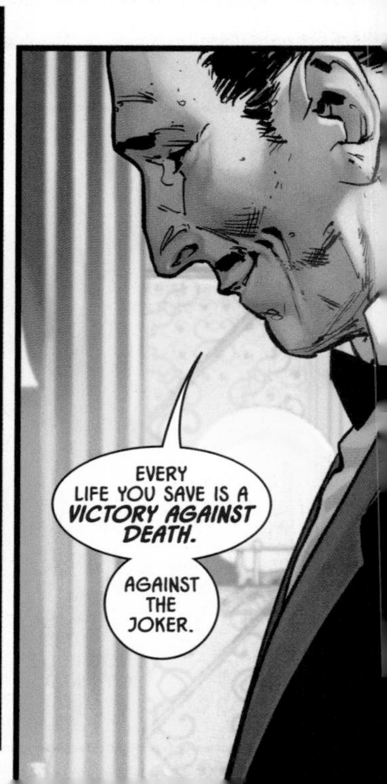
EVERY LIFE YOU SAVE IS A VICTORY AGAINST DEATH.
AGAINST THE JOKER.

I DON'T THINK I CAN DO IT ALONE...
THEN *DON'T*.
FIND YOUR *FAMILY*. FIND YOUR *LOVE*. TAKE BACK YOUR CITY.
LET GO OF THE WEIGHT. LET GO OF THE GUILT. LET GO OF ME, AND DO WHAT YOU MUST DO.
BE THE IMPOSSIBLE MAN WHO SAVES ALL THE FAMILIES ON THEIR WAY HOME FROM THE THEATER.
IF I WAKE UP WITH MY MIND INTACT...I WON'T HEAR YOUR VOICE ANYMORE.
I DON'T KNOW THAT I CAN DO IT WITHOUT YOU.
MY BOY, THIS *IS* YOU DOING IT WITHOUT ME.
I AM ONLY A VOICE IN YOUR HEAD, TELLING YOU WHAT YOU NEED TO HEAR TO STEADY YOURSELF AND DO WHAT NEEDS TO BE DONE.
YOU DON'T NEED ME ON THE OTHER END OF THE BAT-COMPUTER TO KNOW EXACTLY WHAT I'D TELL YOU IN ANY CIRCUMSTANCE.
SO WAKE UP, MY BOY. TELL THIS CITY WHO YOU ARE.

GASP
YOU...YOU'RE AWAKE...THAT'S NOT POSSIBLE. THE TOXIN IN YOUR SYSTEM...
HAS NO HOLD OVER ME ANYMORE.
BUT HOW... THAT'S **NOT** POSSIBLE!
I'M...
BATMAN
ABOUT $@%# TIME YOU DID THAT.
SHE HAD THIS WHOLE SAD-SACK STORY, AND IF I HAD TO LISTEN TO ANOTHER MINUTE I WAS GOING TO HAVE TO OFF MYSELF.
YOU KNOW WHAT? MAYBE IT'S **GOOD** I DIDN'T END UP A REAL SHRINK.

YOU GOT YOUR HEAD ON STRAIGHT?
THAT DEPENDS...
THE WHOLE PLACE IS ON FIRE. SHE BURNED IT UP.
THEN YES. MY HEAD IS ON STRAIGHT.
I NEED TO REACTIVATE MY COMMUNICATIONS SYSTEM.
I THINK YOU FRIED YOUR CIRCUITS BACK AT THE THEATER.
DON'T UNDERESTIMATE WHAT I CAN FIT IN THIS BELT.
I CALL IT A BAT-TERY.
NO, YOU @$@@ DON'T.
COMPUTER. THIS IS BATMAN. GET ME THE LOCATION OF THE FAMILY.
DESIGNATE, WHICH FAMILY MEMBERS?
I NEED EVERYONE.

I'M LEAVING.
I BELIEVE I'VE TOLD YOU THAT'S IMPOSSIBLE.
IT WON'T BE. YOU'RE GOING TO COME ALONG WITH ME. EDDIE TOO.
HAH. MY DEAR. WHY ON ***EARTH*** WOULD YOU THINK YOU COULD RECRUIT US INTO SUPERHEROICS? DURING A ***JOKER*** ATTACK OF ALL THINGS?
WHAT IF I TOLD YOU I COULD MAKE YOU A BILLIONAIRE?

Jorge Jimenez
2020

GOTHAM MIDTOWN.
HAHAHAHA HAHAHAH
SIR...IT'S BEEN MADE TO YOUR EXACT SPECIFICATIONS.
I KNOW! THAT'S WHY I'M LAUGHING!
IT'S THE MOST LUDICROUS THING I'VE EVER SEEN...
I LOVE IT.
TAKE ME TO ACE CHEMICAL. GO THE LONG WAY AROUND.

WHAT'S YOUR NAME, KID?
ABE, SIR.
ARE YOU A LIFER, ABE? GOTHAM STOCK, OR ARE YOU A TRANSPLANT?
I'VE LIVED HERE ALL MY LIFE, MR. JOKER.
GOTHAM IS A JOKE!!
HA
HAHAHA
HA

THEN IT HAS TO BE NICE FOR YOU, DOESN'T IT? SEEING THE CITY WAKE UP LIKE THIS. IT FEELS LIKE IT'S BEEN PRETENDING TO BE SOMETHING IT'S NOT FOR SUCH A LONG TIME.
BUT I REMEMBER THE GRIT ON THE STREET. WALKING HOME, NOT SURE IF YOU'RE GOING TO BE MUGGED BY A COP OR A ROBBER. IT WAS ONLY DIFFERENT UNIFORMS.
DC COMICS PRESENTS
THE JOKER WAR
PART FIVE
JAMES TYNION IV WRITER JORGE JIMENEZ ARTIST TOMEU MOREY COLORS
CLAYTON COWLES LETTERS JORGE JIMENEZ & TOMEU MOREY COVER
DERRICK CHEW VARIANT COVER DAVE WIELGOSZ ASSOC. EDITOR
BEN ABERNATHY EDITOR BATMAN CREATED BY BOB KANE WITH BILL FINGER

HE TRIED TO CHANGE THAT. TRIED TO ROOT OUT THE CORRUPTION AND MAKE PEOPLE BELIEVE IN SOMETHING SELFISH AND STRANGE.
A CHILD'S FANTASY OF JUSTICE INFECTED THIS CITY, STRIPPED THE DARK LIFE AND DANGER FROM IT. MADE IT A CARTOON SHOW.
AND THE BAT NEVER SAW THE TRUTH.
HE NEVER SAW GOTHAM'S FESTERING, ROTTING, HUNGRY FACE, DESPERATE TO SWALLOW YOU WHOLE.
HE THINKS IT'S HIS CITY. HE BOUGHT HIS WAY INTO GIVING THIS CITY A MASS DELUSION-- TO MAKE IT FORGET WHAT IT IS.

BUT IT'S ALWAYS BEEN MY CITY.
I KNOW THAT GOTHAM DOESN'T CARE ABOUT HOW MANY PEOPLE LIVE OR DIE.

IT DOESN'T CARE ABOUT **GOOD** OR **BAD**.
IT JUST DOESN'T WANT TO BE BOUND BY ANYONE'S RULES.
IT JUST WANTS TO BE FREE. IT WANTS TO HURT PEOPLE. IT WANTS TO BE DANGEROUS AGAIN.
SOMETIMES I THINK THE POISON THAT BLEACHED MY SKIN GOT INTO MY BRAIN AND **INFECTED** ME WITH THAT **FESTERING** DARK SPIRIT OF THE CITY.
THAT I'M HAUNTED BY ALL THE GHOSTS OF THE DEAD. THAT I'M THEIR MESSENGER, COME TO REMIND BATMAN THAT THIS CITY DOES NOT **BELONG** TO HIM.
HAHAHAHAHAHA!
WHAT A @$#% NUTJOB.
BUT THAT'S WHAT THIS IS ALL ABOUT. IT'S GETTING THE BALL ROLLING. IT'S MAKING THIS ALL A BIT MORE DANGEROUS AGAIN.

ACE CHEMICALS
ACE CHEMICALS

SIR, WE'RE HERE.
HOME AGAIN, HOME AGAIN.

BZZZ... BZZZ... BZZZ...
HELLO, DEAR. I WAS STARTING TO THINK YOU WERE DEAD.

WHAT'S THAT NOISE?
NOTHING IMPORTANT. JUST CLEANING UP A MESS.

HOW'D THE MEETING GO?
POORLY.
THEY GOT THE ONE-UP ON ME. I THOUGHT BATMAN WAS DOWN FOR THE COUNT.

THEY LEFT ME TIED UP FOR THE COPS, BUT SOME OF OUR BOYS GOT TO ME FIRST. BUT THAT MEANS HE'S BEEN OUT THERE WORKING FOR A FEW HOURS NOW.
I'M SORRY. I WANTED TO DO MORE.

ALL THIS MEANS IS WE'RE READY FOR THE FINAL ACT. THE STREETS ARE IN CHAOS, BUT IT'S TIME WE PUT YOUR CHEMISTRY TO USE.
IT LOOKS LIKE YOUR TOXINS ARE ALREADY EN ROUTE TO FINISH THE JOB. I'M GOING TO CLEAN THINGS UP AROUND HERE.
I WANT THOSE THEATERS FILLED NOW.
HE'S GOING TO COME FOR YOU.
I KNOW. ISN'T IT FUN?
TELL THE CLOWNS THAT IT'S TIME TO UP THEIR GAME.
I'LL PAY OUT A THOUSAND FOR EVERY DEAD BODY THEY BRING TO ME. AND IF IT'S A BAT? LET'S CALL IT A MILLION.
IT'S NOT A WAR WITHOUT SOME MASS MURDER, DON'T YOU THINK?
AREN'T YOU WORRIED...?
NO, DEAR. NOT AT ALL. I KNOW EXACTLY WHERE HE IS AND WHAT HE'S GOING TO DO NEXT.
I JUST NEED TO PUT ON MY NEW SUIT.
"WE DON'T HAVE MUCH TIME."

HE KNOWS ME. HE KNOWS THIS WILL BE MY NEXT MOVE. HE'S FORCED MY HAND.
HE WANTS ME TOO AFRAID TO PUT YOU IN THE FIELD, BUT HE'S MADE IT SO THERE'S NO OTHER CHOICE.
BUT I'M GLAD YOU'RE ALL HERE...
RED HOOD
DICK GRAYSON
HARLEY QUINN
ORPHAN
BATGIRL
SIGNAL
SPOILER
RED ROBIN
I SHOULD HAVE BROUGHT YOU IN FROM THE BEGINNING. THE LAST YEAR HAS BEEN HARD, BUT I THINK I'M SEEING CLEARLY FOR THE FIRST TIME IN A LONG TIME.
I'M SORRY I HAVEN'T BEEN BETTER. I HAVE TO BE. I WILL BE.
BUT RIGHT NOW, OUR CITY IS IN CHAOS. JOKER IS USING EVERYTHING I'VE BUILT TO LAY THE CITY TO WASTE. AND IT'S ONLY GOING TO GET WORSE FROM HERE.

BATWOMAN AND THE GCPD HAVE ALREADY STORMED WAYNE ENTERPRISES.
THAT'S GOING TO CUT OFF THE NEW SUPPLY OF VEHICLES AND WEAPONS.
LUCIUS FOX HAS BEEN RESCUED.*
BUT WE'VE BARELY SCRATCHED THE SURFACE OF WHAT NEEDS TO BE DONE.
RIGHT NOW, THEATERS ARE FILLING ALL OVER GOTHAM. JOKER IS GOING TO PLAY THE PEOPLE OF OUR CITY A MOVIE, AND THEN HE'S GOING TO KILL THEM.
*SEE DETECTIVE COMICS #1025! --BEN & DAVE
CINEMA
I NEED YOU TO STOP IT. AND STOP THE VIOLENCE HAPPENING IN THE STREETS.
IT'S A LOT TO ASK.
BUT I KNOW I CAN TRUST YOU TO TAKE OUR CITY BACK.

WHERE WILL YOU GO, BATMAN?
JOKER'S AT ACE CHEMICAL. I'LL GO TO HIM THERE. I'LL PUT AN END TO THIS.
AND I'M GOING WITH, SO I CAN KILL JOKER.
WAIT, WHAT?!
THAT'S NOT WHAT'S HAPPENING.
WAIT, WHY THE HELL IS THAT NOT WHAT'S HAPPENING? THAT'S THE WHOLE REASON I CAME HERE!
I THINK SOMEBODY NEEDS TO GO BACK TO ARKHAM.
NOBODY ASKED YOUR OPINION, DUCKBOY.

DUCKBOY?!

WE DON'T HAVE TIME FOR THIS.
YEAH, YOU CAN SAY THAT AGAIN. WE'VE GOT INCOMING.

HAHAHAHAHA...
I'M GONNA BUY A @$%& ISLAND WITH YOUR SCALPS!
NO.
YOU WON'T.
THERE ARE MORE CLOWNS COMING. THEY KNOW WE'RE IN THE FIELD. WE CAN'T STAY HERE TOGETHER.
I WANT TO GET TO THE CLOCK TOWER. I CAN COORDINATE FROM THERE. NIGHTWING CAN LEAD IN THE FIELD.
I'LL TAKE AS MANY CLOWNS DOWN AS I CAN ALONG THE WAY.

YOU NEED TO GO, BRUCE. WE'LL GET THE CITY UNDER CONTROL.
DICK...I THINK IT MIGHT BE TIME FOR A *CHANGE* OF CLOTHES.
I GRABBED THIS FROM ONE OF THE MICROCAVES IN WAYNE ENTERPRISES.
BRUCE...
IT'S GOOD TO HAVE YOU BACK.*
*TO SEE HOW **DICK GRAYSON** GOT HIS MEMORIES BACK, SEE **NIGHTWING** #74! --BEN & DAVE
YOU, TOO.
BUT THERE'S A PART OF ALL OF THIS YOU DIDN'T MENTION.
HE STILL HAS THE WAYNE FORTUNE. WHAT ARE WE GOING TO DO ABOUT THAT?

"FIRST WE TAKE THE JOKER...THEN WE CAN WORRY ABOUT MONEY."
THIS BUILDING IS ABSOLUTELY HIDEOUS.
THEY CAN'T ALL BE QUESTION MARKS AND ICEBERGS, EDDIE.
CATWOMAN, YOU GOT US OUT OF MY SAFE HOUSE INTO THE HEART OF ALL THIS DANGER.
I TRUST YOU HAVE A PLAN.
GRAVES, WILLOCK, AND CRAIN. THE LEGITIMATE FRONT FOR THE UNDERBROKER AND HIS TEAM OF CROOKED MONEY MANIPULATORS. THIS IS OUR TARGET.
SOME OF THAT MONEY IS MY MONEY, CATWOMAN.
IF YOU LISTEN TO EVERYTHING I SAY, YOU'RE ABOUT TO HAVE A WHOLE LOT MORE OF IT.*
*TO SEE CATWOMAN'S HEIST, READ CATWOMAN #25! --BEN & DAVE
LIKE I SAID, I'M HOPING. ARE YOU READY, EDDIE?
I JUST WATCHED A MAN WITH A CLOWN MASK BLOW HIS ARM OFF WITH A POORLY CONSTRUCTED MOLOTOV COCKTAIL.
YOU KNOW, IF THIS PAYS OUT, I THINK I MIGHT BE READY TO RETIRE SOMEWHERE WARM.

ACE
CHEMICALS
ACE
CHEMICALS

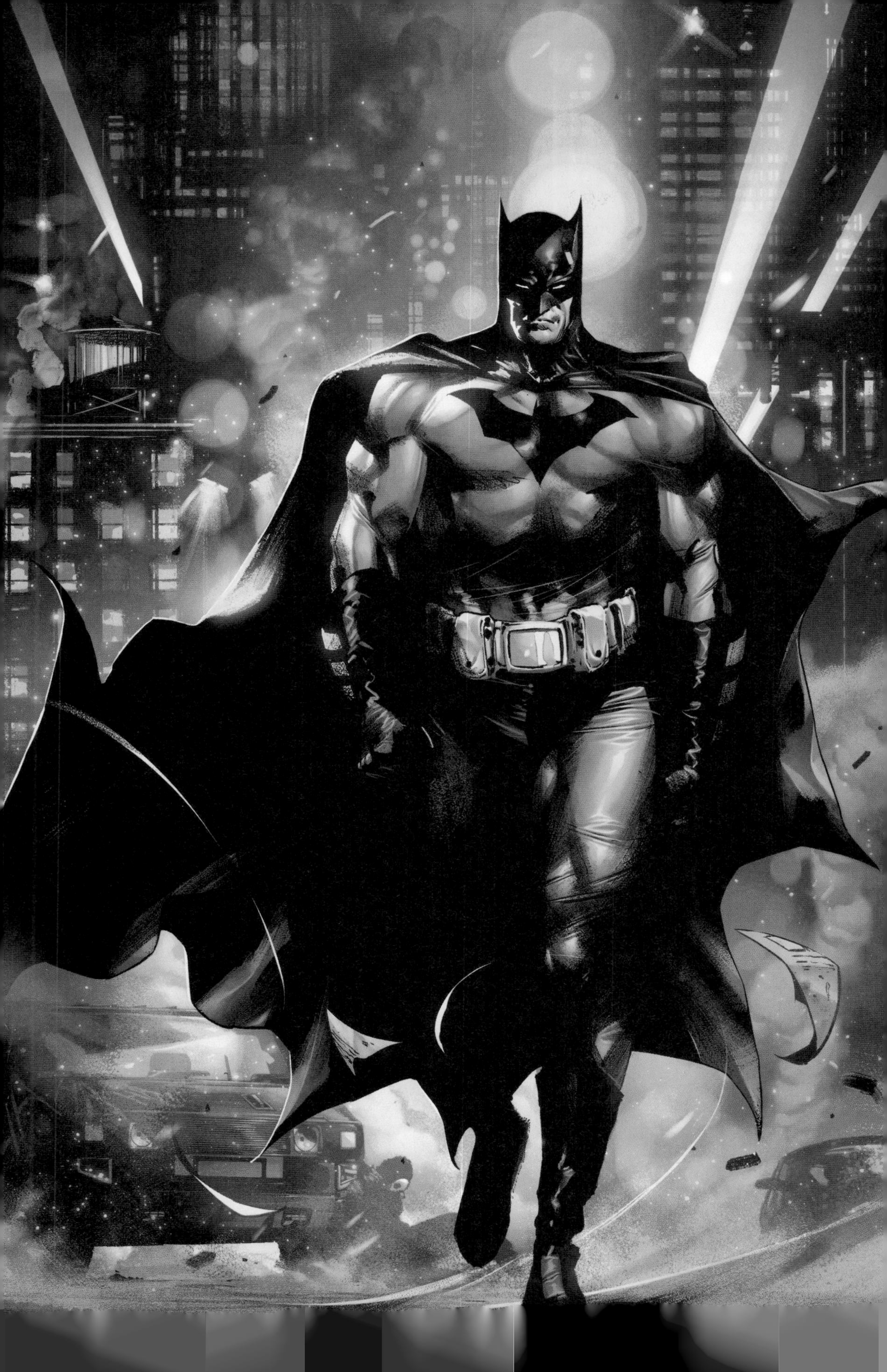

BANG
BANG
WHAT...
DAMMIT, HARLEY.
WHAT THE HELL DID YOU THINK I KEPT SAVING YOUR LIFE FOR, BATS? DIDN'T YOU GET THE POINT? THE BIG PICTURE?
IT'S TIME FOR HIS STORY TO END.
HARLEY, YOU KNOW I CAN'T LET THAT HAPPEN.

THAT'S NOT GOOD ENOUGH. NOT ANYMORE.
I SHOULD HAVE LET THE TOXIN DO ITS JOB. I THOUGHT YOU'D PULLED YOUR HEAD OUT OF YOUR ASS AND SEEN WHAT NEEDED DOING.
YOU KNOW HIM AS WELL AS I DO. HE'S ALWAYS GOING TO ONE-UP HIMSELF. AND EVEN IF YOU TAKE HIM DOWN TODAY...
WHAT'S THE NEXT STEP FROM THIS?! WHAT KINDA GOTHAM ARE YOU GOING TO LET HIM BUILD NEXT TIME?
HOW MANY MORE PUNCHLINES DO YOU WANT HIM TO MAKE OUT THERE?
I KNOW YOU CAN KICK MY ASS AND TAKE MY STUFF IF YOU WANT TO.
HERE'S THE DEAL I'LL MAKE. IF HE KILLS YOU, I'M TAKING THE SHOT. ENDING IT RIGHT THEN AND THERE, AND I DON'T CARE ABOUT YOUR STUPID CODE OR ANY OF THAT.
IF HE'S GOING TO GET AWAY WITH KILLING ALL OF THOSE PEOPLE, TOO. THE GOTHAMITES. I SEE HIM READY TO PULL THE TRIGGER, I WILL SHOOT HIM DOWN.

NO.
THEN YOU STOP ME NOW. YOU PUT ME DOWN **HARD.** YOU MAKE SURE I WON'T GET RIGHT BACK UP AND FINISH THE JOB MYSELF.
THIS CAN'T JUST BE LIKE ALL THE OTHER TIMES. THIS STORY NEEDS TO CHANGE.
IT NEEDS AN ENDING.

JOKER, IT'S OVER.
WE'LL HAVE THE CITY BACK IN JUST A FEW HOURS. AND YOU'LL BE INCARCERATED LONG BEFORE THAT.
SO DO WHATEVER YOU'RE GOING TO DO. MAKE WHATEVER PLAY YOU WANT TO PLAY. BUT KNOW... I'M READY FOR IT.
OH, REALLY?
YOU KNOW, YOU DIDN'T TREAT THE DEAD ALL THAT WELL BACK AT THE MONARCH. BUT THIS ONE...THIS ONE I'VE BEEN SAVING FOR THE GRAND FINALE...
DUG HIM UP FROM YOUR BACKYARD MYSELF. I KNOW YOU MUST STILL HAVE MORE TO SAY TO HIM. AFTER LOSING HIM LIKE YOU DID.
SNAP
MMMMASTER BRRRRUUCE
NO...NO, THIS ISN'T REAL.

SEE, BRUCE. I PROMISED...
...YOU'RE NOT READY FOR THIS AT ALL.
HA HA HA HA HA HA HA HA HA

THE CLOCK TOWER.
BURNSIDE.
COMPUTER, ACTIVATE.
WELCOME, BATGIRL.
I NEED EYES EVERYWHERE. WE'RE GOING TO NEED TO PIN EVERY CLOWN IN THE CITY. I NEED ALL CCTV SYSTEMS, TRAFFIC CAMS, AND CELL DATA WE CAN GET OUR HANDS ON.
COMPLYING.
USE THE BACK DOOR TO GET THE BAT-COMPUTER ONLINE, AND GIVE ME A MAP OF THE FAMILY. PIN EACH OF THEIR LOCATIONS.
COMPLYING.
FIRST THINGS FIRST. ANY BAT-VEHICLE CURRENTLY IN ENEMY HANDS NEEDS TO BE PUT IN MOTHBALLS. IT'S TIME TO EXPEND THE BATFALL PROTOCOL. SHUT EVERYTHING DOWN.
OVERRIDE POLICE DISPATCH. START DIRECTING OFFICERS TO AREAS WITH HIGH CLOWN DENSITY.
OKAY. IT'S TIME TO LET EVERYONE KNOW THAT ORACLE IS BACK ONLINE.

GOTHAM CITY. THIS IS THE VOICE OF ORACLE.
I'M HERE TO TELL YOU WHAT YOU ALREADY KNOW.
WHAT THE CITY HAS BEEN RESISTING ADMITTING BECAUSE OF THE HORRIBLE WEB OF MONEY AND CORRUPTION PARALYZING MAYOR DUNCH AND OUR CITY'S INSTITUTIONS.
THIS CITY IS UNDER ATTACK BY THE JOKER. EVERY MOVIE THEATER IN GOTHAM HAS BEEN TRANSFORMED INTO A DEATH TRAP.
DC COMICS PRESENTS
THE JOKER WAR
FINALE
JAMES TYNION IV
WRITER
JORGE JIMENEZ
ARTIST
TOMEU MOREY
COLORS
CLAYTON COWLES
LETTERS

STAY INSIDE. LOCK YOUR DOORS. I'M HACKING THE EMERGENCY BROADCAST FREQUENCY TO MESSAGE EACH OF YOUR CELL PHONES A TIP LINE. IF YOU ARE IN DANGER, REACH OUT TO US.
I HEARD THE BAT-SIGNAL IS STILL IN STORAGE AFTER THE MOVE TO THE NEW GCPD HEADQUARTERS.
JORGE JIMENEZ & TOMEU MOREY COVER
FRANCESCO MATTINA VARIANT COVER
DAVE WIELGOSZ ASSOC. EDITOR
BEN ABERNATHY EDITOR
BUT BATS DON'T NEED A LIGHT IN THE SKY TO COME HELP YOU.
BLOCK BY BLOCK, WE WILL TAKE BACK THIS CITY.
BATMAN CREATED BY BOB KANE WITH BILL FINGER

COMMISSIONER BULLOCK! THE MAYOR'S OFFICE WANTS YOU TO DIRECT EVERYONE TO SHUT THE ORACLE SYSTEM DOWN.
THERE ARE LUNATICS IN CLOWN MASKS BURNING DOWN THE CITY, AND HE WANTS ME TO DO WHAT?!
GCPD
HE SAID THAT YOU DO IT, OR YOU'RE DONE. YOU'RE ON THIN ICE AS IT IS.
ALL THIS TIME, WE THOUGHT WE COULD MAKE IT BETTER FROM THE INSIDE, EH, JIM? WHAT WOULD YOU DO RIGHT NOW, IF YOU WERE IN MY PLACE?
UGH. LIKE I EVEN HAVE TO ASK.
GOTHAM CITY POLICE
DETECTIVE
TELL MAYOR DUNCH THAT'S MY $%#@ ANSWER.
BOYS. THIS IS YOUR EX-COMMISSIONER BULLOCK SPEAKING.
THE GCPD IS BEING ASKED TO STAND DOWN, BEING TOLD THAT DEFYING CITY HALL'S GOING TO COST YOU YOUR BADGE AND YOUR GUN.
BUT I DON'T NEED A BADGE OR GUN TO DO WHAT'S RIGHT. I'VE GOT MY RADIO, AND I'M GOING TO FOLLOW ORACLE AND GO @#%# HELP PEOPLE.
SO, THE LOT OF YOU ARE GOING TO HAVE TO DECIDE RIGHT NOW...
...DO YOU WANT TO BE A COP IN THIS CROOKED CITY, OR DO YOU WANT TO DO WHAT'S RIGHT?
"NIGHTWING TO ORACLE..."

HAT LINE ABOUT THE BAT-SIGNAL GAVE ME CHILLS.
THAT'S JUST ADJUSTING BACK INTO THE OLD SPANDEX IN THE NIGHT AIR.
IT'S NOT SPANDEX.
YOU REALLY WANT TO GO HEAD-TO-HEAD ON WHO KNOWS EXACTLY HOW THE SYNTHETIC FABRICS IN THEIR COSTUMES ARE MADE?
NOPE. JUST WANTED TO SAY IT'S GREAT TO HEAR YOUR VOICE IN MY EAR AGAIN.
AND IT'S GREAT TO SEE YOU BACK IN BLUE.
THE CLOWN BEHIND YOU HAS A GUN.
I ALREADY SAW HIM.
NO, YOU DIDN'T.
"ANY WORD FROM THE BIG GUY?"
"NOT YET. BUT I BET HE HAS HIS HANDS FULL RIGHT NOW."
"WHAT'S THE PROBLEM, BRUCIE?"

IS IT THE OUTFIT? OR DO YOU NOT LIKE MY PRESENT?
I THOUGHT YOU LOVED YOUR BUTLER!
MASSSTER... BRUUUUCE... WHY...
YOU'RE JUST TRYING TO GET IN MY HEAD. THROW ME OFF.
IT WON'T WORK!
YOU REALLY DO HATE GUNS, DON'T YOU? I USED TO THINK IT WAS JUST BECAUSE YOU'RE BORING, BUT I THINK I'M STARTING TO UNDERSTAND.
IT'S AMAZING HOW MANY EXPLOSIVES YOU CAN FIT INTO THESE LITTLE TOYS OF YOURS, IF YOU'RE NOT AFRAID TO SPEND SOME MONEY.

HERE, BATS. WHY DON'T YOU CHECK OUT MY IMPROVEMENTS UP CLOSE!
HA HAHAHA HA!
NO!
UNNNGH...
YOU... YOU LET ME DIE...WHY DID YOU LET ME DIE?!
HE HE HE HE HE
I HATE YOU. I HATE YOU. I HATE YOU...
BATMAN TO ORACLE.
HA HA HA..

I NEED BACKUP. JOKER'S TAKEN ALFRED'S BODY AND WEAPONIZED IT... I NEED TO GET IT CLEAR OF THIS PLACE...
I WISH I'D BEEN AQUAMAN'S BUTLER INSTEAD.
CALLING FOR HELP? NOW, THAT'S CHEATING. THIS PART IS MEANT TO BE JUST YOU AND ME, AND SOME VERY EXPENSIVE TOYS.
SHHNNNG
GOOD THING ONE OF THEM JUST KILLED YOUR RADIO.
OTHERWISE ALL THOSE WEIRD LITTLE ORPHANS YOU KEEP COLLECTING WOULD HAVE TO LISTEN TO THEIR DEAR OLD BAT-DAD GET STABBED TO DEATH.
SHUT UP.
BE HONEST. IT'S THE COSTUME.
I FINALLY LOOK AS STUPID AS YOU DO.
SHUT UP!

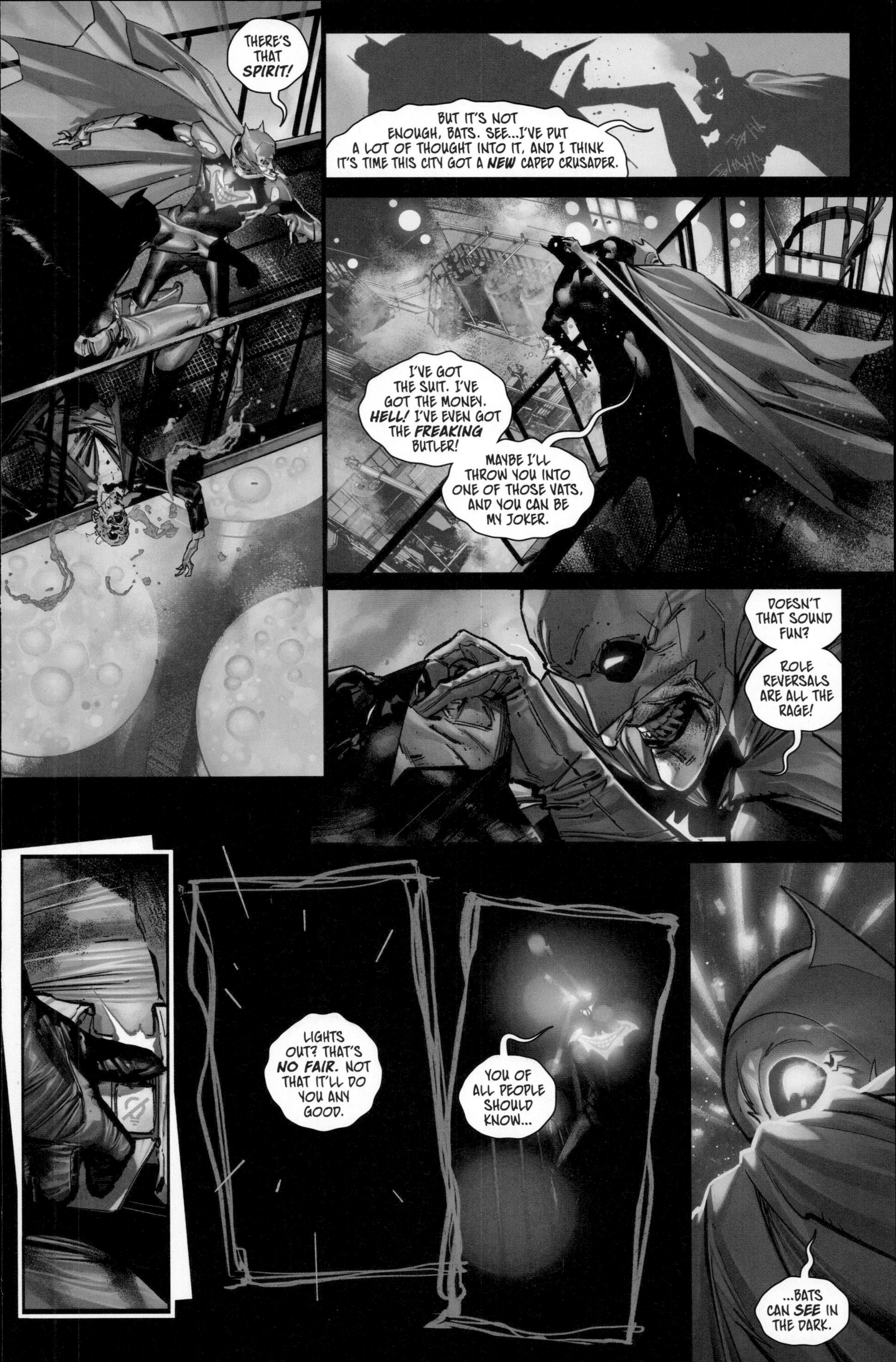
THERE'S THAT SPIRIT!
BUT IT'S NOT ENOUGH, BATS. SEE...I'VE PUT A LOT OF THOUGHT INTO IT, AND I THINK IT'S TIME THIS CITY GOT A NEW CAPED CRUSADER.
I'VE GOT THE SUIT. I'VE GOT THE MONEY. HELL! I'VE EVEN GOT THE FREAKING BUTLER!
MAYBE I'LL THROW YOU INTO ONE OF THOSE VATS, AND YOU CAN BE MY JOKER.
DOESN'T THAT SOUND FUN?
ROLE REVERSALS ARE ALL THE RAGE!
LIGHTS OUT? THAT'S NO FAIR. NOT THAT IT'LL DO YOU ANY GOOD.
YOU OF ALL PEOPLE SHOULD KNOW...
...BATS CAN SEE IN THE DARK.

YOU'RE NOT A BAT.
BRAK!!
KLIK
OKAY THEN, LET'S TRY THIS ANOTHER WAY!
BOOM

HE WASN'T SUPPOSED TO BLOW THE FACTORY YET...
WE'RE NOT READY. THAT'S MEANT TO BE THE *NEXT* STEP.
I NEED WORD FROM MY CLOWNS ON THE STREET. GIVE ME A BODY COUNT. GIVE ME *SOMETHING...*
WHY ISN'T ANY OF THIS STUFF *WORKING?*
MS. PUNCHLINE, I REGRET TO INFORM YOU THAT I AM GOING TO HAVE TO BRING MY *ASSOCIATION* WITH YOU AND THE JOKER TO AN *END.*
KRAK
YOU'RE GOING TO NEED TO VACATE THE PREMISES, *IMMEDIATELY,* OR I WILL CALL THE AUTHORITIES.
ARE YOU KIDDING ME, UNDER-BROKER? WE'VE GIVEN YOU MORE MONEY THAN *GOD!*
AND NOW THAT MONEY HAS BEEN *TAKEN.*
I APPRECIATE YOUR BUSINESS. SHOULD YOU COME INTO SOME MONEY IN THE FUTURE, I BELIEVE YOU HAVE MY CARD.
YOU PIECE OF @$#&%!

IT'S *ME.*
IT'S ALL OVER... SOONER THAN YOU THOUGHT.
I'M SORRY. I THOUGHT WE'D BE ABLE TO PUSH THINGS A LITTLE FURTHER.
BUT I REMEMBER THE PLAN, AND I LOVE YOU.
AND I WILL *NEVER* STOP BELIEVING.
I KNOW A SONG THAT SOUNDS LIKE THAT.
HI. NAME'S NIGHTWING. WE HAVEN'T MET. NOT *REALLY.* I'VE BEE OUT OF TOWN FOR A BIT.
YOU'RE GOING TO PRISON *TONIGHT.* YOU'RE GOING TO STAY IN PRISON FOR THE *REST* OF YOUR *LIFE.*

YEAH. WANNA BET?
YEAH. LET'S BET.
SLAK
WHOM
BRAK
YOU'RE NOT UP AGAINST SOMEONE WHO FORGOT A LIFETIME OF TRAINING ANYMORE.
THIS IS OVER.
WAM!
FWEET
SORRY, BOY BLUE. THE ODDS JUST CHANGED.
YEAH. THEY SURE DID.

MAKE THIS FAST, WE NEED YOU IN MIDTOWN. WE STILL HAVE WORD OF CLOWNS AT SIXTEEN THEATERS. BUT I'M GETTING SOME RATTLING OVER THE WIRE.
THEY'RE NOT GETTING THEIR MONEY. I THINK THEY KNOW THIS IS OVER. OR AT LEAST THAT IT'S ENDING.
WHO DO YOU THINK STOLE THE FORTUNE BACK?
C'MON, DICK... I KNOW YOU ONLY JUST GOT YOUR HEAD BACK ON YOUR SHOULDERS, BUT I THOUGHT YOU WERE TRAINED BY THE WORLD'S GREATEST DETECTIVE?
MRRROW.
COME ON, NOW, LOVE.
IT'S TIME TO END THIS.

ORACLE TO BATMAN.
YOU HAVE A BLOCKER ON YOUR RADIO, BUT I'VE BYPASSED IT THE BEST I CAN FROM HERE. I CAN'T HEAR YOU, BUT YOU SHOULD BE ABLE TO HEAR ME.
WE'VE APPREHENDED THE TANKERS. MOST OF THE CLOWNS ARE FALLING BACK.
PUNCHLINE WILL BE IN OUR CUSTODY IN A MATTER OF MINUTES.
YOU TAKE DOWN JOKER AND THIS IS OVER.
MY FAMILY HAS ALREADY TAKEN THE CITY BACK.
YOU WON'T GET YOUR WAR.
!!
YOU... CAN'T... WIN...
HA HA HA HA
OH, BATMAN. DON'T YOU GET IT?
YOU MISSED THE WAR. I ALREADY WON.
YOU HAVE TO BE SMART ENOUGH TO HAVE FIGURED THAT OUT ALREADY.

WE'RE ALREADY ONTO THE AFTERMATH. YOUR LITTLE BRATS ARE ONLY PICKING THROUGH THE DEBRIS OF A BRAND-NEW CITY, THEY JUST DON'T SEE IT YET.
THE MOVIE THEATERS WERE JUST TO GET UNDER YOUR SKIN.
IT WOULD HAVE BEEN A GOOD JOKE TO FINISH THE JOB, TO SHOW THEM THE SAD FACE OF THEIR DARK KNIGHT.
BUT IT'S REALLY ABOUT YOU AND ME, RIGHT HERE.
IT'S ABOUT THIS SUIT.
THE SUIT YOU'D GET TO WEAR WHEN YOU FINALLY SAVED GOTHAM CITY ONCE AND FOR ALL.

WHATEVER FUTURE YOU HAD DREAMED OF, WHERE YOU GOT TO WEAR THIS SHINY NEW COSTUME? IT'S GONE, BRUCE. IT'S ALL GONE.
WHAT DID YOU PICTURE? RETIREMENT? SPENDING LONG HOURS IN THE MANOR WITH ROBINS AND GRAND-ROBINS COOING AT YOUR FEET?
AND THE CITY SOME BRIGHT AND SHINING PARAGON? METROPOLIS WITH FEWER ALIENS?
NO. THAT DOESN'T SOUND LIKE GOTHAM, DOES IT?
THIS IS WHAT I WANTED YOU TO UNDERSTAND, FINALLY.
THIS CITY DOES NOT WANT YOU. THIS CITY IS SICK OF YOU, AND SICK OF ALL THE WAYS YOU'VE FAILED IT.
YOU TRIED TO MAKE IT PRETEND IT WAS A NICE PLACE, BUT IT ISN'T. IT'S AN ANGRY CITY. A HUNGRY CITY. A DANGEROUS CITY.
IT DOESN'T WANT TO BE TAMED. IT DOESN'T WANT TO BE CONTROLLED. AND I'VE PLANTED THE RIGHT SEEDS.

EVERYBODY KNOWS
WAYNE ENTERPRISES?
S NOT THERE TO
HELP THEM.
IT'S THE
AME SORT OF
UPT **CORPORATE**
OR AS ALL THE OTHER
G COMPANIES IN
THE WORLD.

HAHAHAHAHAHAHAHA!
THE WAYNE FAMILY IS A BROKEN SYSTEM. LIKE GOTHAM CITY HALL. LIKE THE GCPD.
NOBODY HAS FAITH IN ***ANYTHING*** ANYMORE. AND WHY ***SHOULD*** THEY? IT DIDN'T STOP A FEW CLOWNS FROM FLYING A BATPLANE THROUGH THEIR WINDOW.

AND NEITHER DID BATMAN.
SHOULDN'T HE HAVE BEEN ABLE TO STOP ALL OF THIS BEFORE IT HAPPENED?
LOOK, BRUCE, YOU DON'T UNDERSTAND GOTHAM. YOU DON'T EVEN LIVE IN THE CITY. YOU'RE OUT IN THE FANCY SUBURBS IN YOUR BROODY CASTLE.
BATMAN WAS A STUPID LITTLE KID'S STUPID IDEA. AND NOW THIS CITY SEES IT FOR HOW HOLLOW IT IS.
I DIDN'T NEED TO SHOW THEM THAT BATMAN IS BRUCE WAYNE SO THEY COULD SEE WHO YOU REALLY ARE.
IT'S ABOUT TO GET SO MUCH HARDER. I'M MAKING YOU START OVER FROM SCRATCH.
YOU WON'T EVEN LOOK LIKE BRUCE WAYNE ANYMORE WHEN I'M DONE CARVING YOU UP...YOU'LL HAVE TO START FIGHTING BACK WITH NOTHING.
HAHA HAHAHA HAHA!

HEYA, MISTAH J.
LONG TIME, NO SEE.
WHO--?!

HARLS...
I'VE BEEN USING YOUR MUG SHOT FOR TARGET PRACTICE A LONG TIME NOW. BUT I GOTTA SAY, THAT WAS PRETTY CATHARTIC.
STILL DIDN'T GET THE KILL SHOT, THOUGH.
NO. THAT HAS TO COME FROM HIM.
HARLEY... WHAT ARE YOU DOING?
WE'RE GOING TO PLAY A LITTLE GAME, BATSY.
AND YOU'RE GOING TO NEED TO MAKE A DECISION...

THESE BOMBS ARE GOING TO GO OFF IN A FEW SECONDS NOW. AND TRUST ME, THEY'RE REAL GOOD.
I SWIPED 'EM RIGHT OUT OF BELLE REVE WITH THE REST OF THE HEAVY ARTILLERY.
HARLEY... NO.
YOU WERE LOSING.
NO I WASN'T. I WAS CALLING IN THE FAMILY. THEY'RE EN ROUTE HERE NOW. THE LONGER I KEPT HIM TALKING THE MORE TIME I GOT.
WE DON'T NEED TO END IT THIS WAY. HE NEEDS TO BE LOCKED BACK UP.
HONEY. YOU'RE TALKIN' TO THE WRONG GIRL IF YOU THINK HE'S NOT DANGEROUS LOCKED UP IN ARKHAM.
IT'S LIKE I SAID. THAT'S NOT GOOD ENOUGH FOR ME. NOT ANYMORE.

HEHEHEHEHEE... OH, THIS IS TOO GOOD.
SO NOW, YOU GOT TO CHOOSE. WHAT KIND OF CITY DO YOU WANT GOTHAM TO BE?
DO YOU WANT IT TO BE ONE WHERE HE KNOWS HE CAN GET AWAY WITH ANYTHING, AND EVERYTHING, AND YOU'RE ALWAYS GOING TO LET HIM SLIDE?
HA
HA
OR DO YOU WANT TO CHANGE THE GAME?
YOU'RE ONLY GOING TO GET ONE OF US IN TIME, BATS.
WHO'S IT GOING TO BE?
HARLEY!

I DO LOVE A WILD CARD. SHE'S STILL GOT THAT OLD SPUNK, DOESN'T SHE?
LISTEN CLOSE. IF YOU WERE SMART ENOUGH TO PICK THE POCKETS FROM THE NEXT GEN BATSUIT, THE BOMB CAN BE DISARMED--
NO! THAT'S NOT HOW IT WORKS.
YOU'RE GOING TO HAVE TO SAVE ME YOURSELF. YOU'RE NOT GOING TO RISK MY DYING AND LEAVE YOUR BUTLER'S BODY TO ROAST WITH ME.

WAIT... WHERE ARE YOU GOING?
BATMAN. COME BACK HERE.

DON'T JUST WALK AWAY FROM ME!

DON'T YOU DARE JUST WALK AWAY!
HA HA HA HA HA
HAHAHAHA HA
SHUT UP.
tick...
SHUT UP!
tick...
TRABOOM

ONE WEEK LATER.
UNNNGH...
I JUST HAD THE WEIRDEST #%&@ DREAM.

AND YOU WERE THERE...AND THERE WAS THIS MEAN LADY WITH A DUMB NAME WHO WASN'T EVEN FUNNY OR ANYTHING.
HARLEY.
HOW LONG HAVE I BEEN OUT?
A WEEK.
TOLDJA IT WAS A GOOD BOMB.
Y'KNOW, YOU REALLY HAD ME FOOLED A SECOND THERE.
NOW... IS HE DEAD?
I FOUND HIS BOMB INTACT. DEACTIVATED JUST IN TIME WITH THE TOOLS HE STOLE FROM THE BATSUIT HE HAD BEEN WEARING. THERE'S BEEN NO SIGN OF HIM SINCE.
YEAH. HE'S NEVER BEEN THE "ENCORE" KINDA CLOWN.
WHEN THE BIG SHOW IS OVER, HE HEADS TO GROUND.

BUT NOW HE KNOWS. AND YOU KNOW, TOO. I THINK...I THINK THAT MATTERS.
IT LOOKS SO DIFFERENT ALREADY.
HUH?
THE CITY. IT'S CHANGED SO MUCH.
I MEAN, SURE. IT'S UGLIER. BUT IT'S ALWAYS BEEN KINDA UGLY.
A BIG UGLY CITY FULL OF UGLY PEOPLE DOING UGLY THINGS.
BUT THEY'RE STILL JUST... YOU KNOW...ALIVE. DOING THINGS. TRYING THEIR BEST.
AND YOU HELP KEEP THEM ALIVE. THAT'S PRETTY NEAT, I THINK.

YOU'RE RIGHT.
OH, BROTHER. I'M ON SOME KINDA HAPPY JUICE, AREN'T I? I'M NOT USED TO BEING THIS GENEROUS TO THOSE BOZOS OUT THERE.

I'M GLAD YOU'RE OKAY.
ARE YOU?
"I HAD TO BURY MY FATHER AGAIN TODAY.
"I DID IT WITH MY FAMILY.
HE ONCE TOLD ME THAT A FIGHT WITH JOKER IS A FIGHT AGAINST DEATH ITSELF.
AND THAT FIGHTING IS LIVING, CONTINUING ON.
AND I'M READY FOR THAT FIGHT.
EVERYTHING I'VE LOST... I DON'T KNOW THAT I EVER NEEDED.
AND WHAT COMES NEXT IS GOING TO BE HARD.

BUT I THINK I CAN MEET IT FACE ON. I THINK I CAN BE A BETTER MAN. A BETTER BATMAN.
WELL, GOOD.
NO POINT IN BEING A CRAPPIER BATMAN, YOU KNOW?
I GUESS NOT.
NOW. YOU GOTTA HELP ME BUST OUT OF THIS JOINT BEFORE THEY ASK ME ABOUT HEALTH INSURANCE, OKAY?

EPILOGUE.

OH, BRUCE, BRUCE, BRUCE...
WHAT A MESS YOU'VE MADE...OUR TEACHERS WOULD BE ASHAMED OF YOU.
I THINK IT'S TIME YOUR CITY HAD A CHOICE IN ITS PROTECTOR.
THE TRUCE IS OVER. IT'S TIME FOR GOTHAM TO MEET ***THE GHOST-MAKER!***

GOTHAM CITY.
THE NARROWS.
1A
Oh.

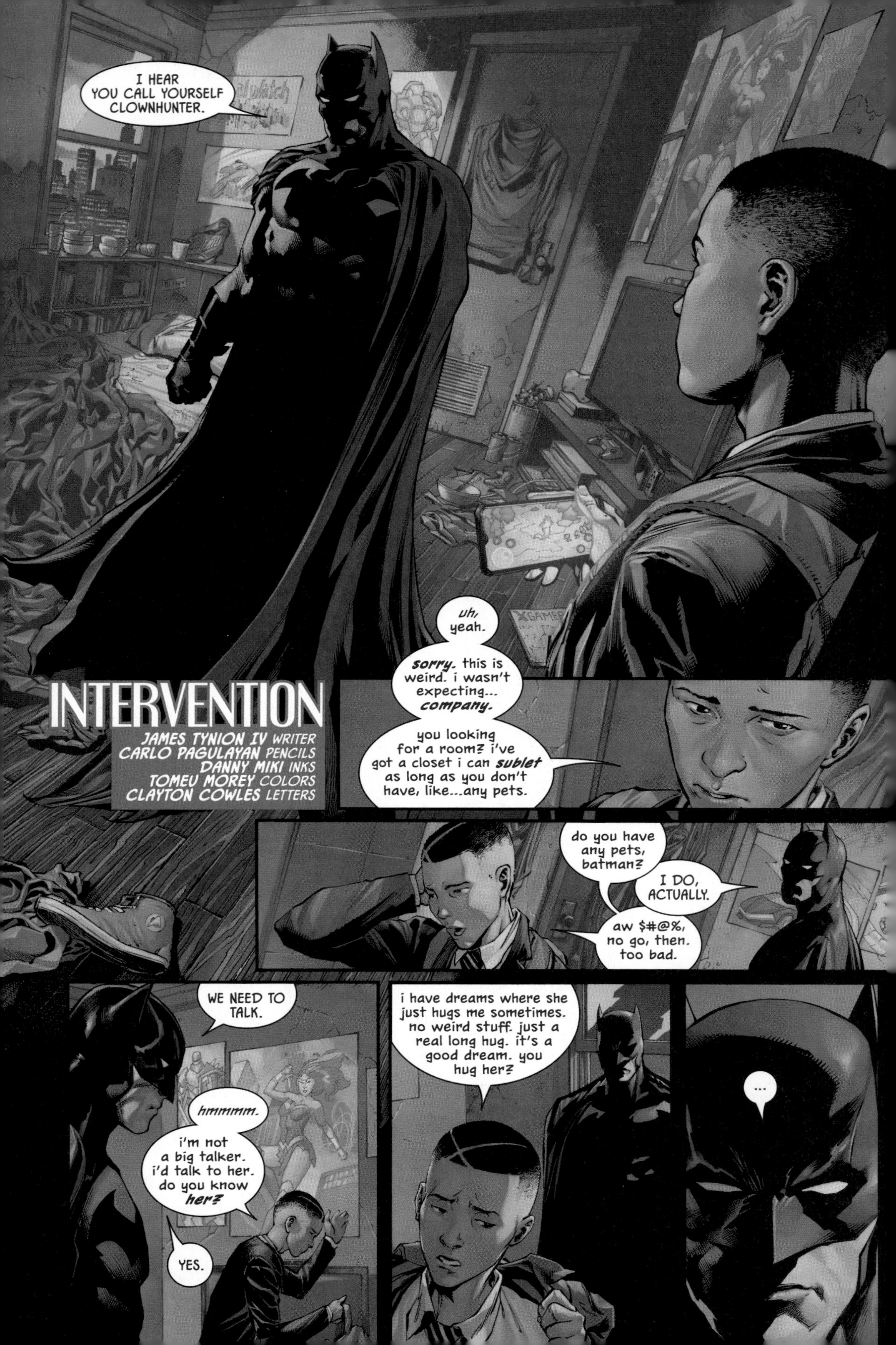
I HEAR YOU CALL YOURSELF CLOWNHUNTER.
uh, yeah.
INTERVENTION
JAMES TYNION IV WRITER
CARLO PAGULAYAN PENCILS
DANNY MIKI INKS
TOMEU MOREY COLORS
CLAYTON COWLES LETTERS
sorry. this is weird. i wasn't expecting... company.
you looking for a room? i've got a closet i can sublet as long as you don't have, like... any pets.
do you have any pets, batman?
I DO, ACTUALLY.
aw $#@%, no go, then. too bad.
WE NEED TO TALK.
hmmmmm.
i'm not a big talker. i'd talk to her. do you know her?
YES.
i have dreams where she just hugs me sometimes. no weird stuff. just a real long hug. it's a good dream. you hug her?
...

YOUR NAME IS BAO PHAM.
your name is dirk wingleton.
haha. yeah. that's a neat trick.
see. we're both men of talents.
YOUR PARENTS WERE KILLED BY THE JOKER FIVE YEARS AGO.
...
if you're gonna do the mask thing, i gotta get mine. that's only fair, dirk.
HOW MANY?
how many masks do I have?
only one so far, but I think it's pretty good. i should wash it, though. do you like it?
HOW MANY CLOWNS DID YOU KILL HERE IN THE NARROWS?
&%$#, you know what, i was trying to count, but i got it all screwed up.
but, uh...not enough?
yeah. not enough.

WHY DID YOU DO IT?
"i mean, you know... it was the third night hearing one of them firebombing a store down the street.
COMIX REPUBLIC
"that's when I had this moment, when I stopped believing some guy in a bat costume was gonna come and stop them.
"and that made me realize: that guy in that costume coulda stopped all of this a long time ago.
"before my parents. before any of them.
that's when i started feeling stupid for having believed in him for so long. believing that he'd saved me. that he'd saved anyone.

BAO.
did you kill him this time?
...
everyone's acting like he's gone, like they act every other @$#@ time, but he *isn't* gone, is he?
...
a cop came by to say that his clowns dug my mom and pop up. and they found remains burning in a theater in crime alley.
i didn't even find that out until it was all over.
said there were *batarangs* on the scene.
I'M SORRY.

you punched my dead mom and dad and set them on *fire* and let the *devil live.*
and you know all those people. all those clowns who put on the masks the second he gave them permission to cause all this trouble.
they hid their masks and they're just hiding and walking down the streets like *nothing's wrong.*
and what? you're going to arrest *me?* is that it?
I'VE LISTENED TO THE POLICE REPORTS OUT OF THE NARROWS. YOUR NEIGHBORHOOD **SUPPORTS** YOU. NO ONE WILL CORROBORATE WHAT YOU DID HERE. TURNING YOU IN WOULDN'T DO ANY GOOD.
ANOTHER TIME, I'D HAVE COME HERE TO FRIGHTEN YOU DOWN ANOTHER PATH, BUT I WANT TO HELP YOU, BAO.

THIS IS THE NUMBER FOR THE THOMPKINS FREE CLINIC. **DR. LESLIE THOMPKINS** HELPED ME WHEN I WAS IN MY DARKEST PLACES. SHE CAN HELP YOU.
YOU DON'T NEED TO GO DOWN THIS ROAD. YOU DON'T NEED TO KILL ANYONE ELSE. THERE ARE OTHER WAYS YOU CAN HELP MAKE THIS CITY BETTER.
THOMPKINS CLINIC
what if i don't go? what if i don't want to make this city better?
what if i just want to kill every %$#@& in a clown mask?
THEN I'LL STOP YOU, IF I HAVE TO.
THOMPKINS CLINIC
I WON'T LET YOU TAKE ANOTHER LIFE. I KNOW WHERE YOU ***LIVE.*** I'VE ALREADY DISMANTLED ALL OF YOUR GUNS AND EXPLOSIVES.
THIS WILL BE YOUR ONLY WARNING. I WON'T ALLOW A CLOWNHUNTER IN THIS CITY. I MEAN IT.
CALL LESLIE. GET THE HELP YOU NEED.

hmmm.
help. help sounds nice.
maybe when i'm *finished.*

GOTHAM CITY.
ROBBINSVILLE.
WHERE HAVE YOU BEEN?
EXCUSE ME?
IT'S JUST...UH... THAT'S QUITE THE STACK OF PAPERS.
HA. YOU KNOW? I GUESS IT IS.
GOTHAM GAZ
MASS CASUALT AVERTED AS JOK PLOT FOILED
ER'S TOP LIE N GCPD CUST
HE MYSTE PUNCHLIN EVEALED.
YNE ENTERP RUCTURES A KER TAKEOV
UILD PROJECT AT RISK.
NEWS
NO ARKHAM F CLOWN PRIN CRIME!
GOTHAM COU
I HAD AN... ACCIDENT A FEW WEEKS BACK. TOOK ME OUT OF COMMISSION. IF I'M BEING HONEST, I'M STILL A BIT OUT OF COMMISSION.
BUT I NEEDED TO GET SOME FRESH AIR. SEE SOME FRIENDLY FACES. CATCH UP ON THE NEWS...
WELL, THERE'S PLENTY OF IT. THEY STOPPED INVESTIGATING THAT WAYNE FELLA, AND THERE'S THE CLOWN GIRL ALL OVER THE PAPERS.

SHE'S A TREAT, ISN'T SHE?
Go Go
OH, I DON'T KNOW. I DON'T GO MUCH FOR THE CRAZY TYPES.
HAHAHAHA, YOU'RE FUNNY.
OH, BUT THEY'RE SO MUCH FUN. AT LEAST UNTIL THEY SLIP A KNIFE BETWEEN YOUR RIBS.
I USED TO BE A COMEDIAN.
YOU SEE THE VIDEO?
VIDEO?
THE PUNCHLINE GIRL. SHE'S UNDER HOUSE ARREST NOW AFTER SHE PROVED SHE WASN'T NUTS ENOUGH TO TOSS HER IN ARKHAM.
SHE PUT OUT A WHOLE VIDEO ON THE INTERNET.
GOT HER IN TROUBLE WITH THE JUDGE AND EVERYTHING, BUT IT'S BEEN SPREADING LIKE WILDFIRE...
I CAN SHOW YOU IF YOU WANT.
PLEASE.

OKAY, ARE WE READY? HAVE WE STARTED YET?
YES. WE'RE RECORDING NOW.

OKAY.
I'M SORRY, I'M SHAKING. I GET NERVOUS IN FRONT OF CAMERAS.

IT'S OKAY. JUST TAKE YOUR TIME. START BY INTRODUCING YOURSELF.

I GUESS...THAT'S THE REAL QUESTION EVERYONE'S ASKING, ISN'T IT?
WHO AM I?

I THINK EVERYONE'S HEARD THE NAME I'VE BEEN CALLING MYSELF THE LAST FEW MONTHS. THE NAME I GAVE MYSELF TO MAKE A VERY BAD MAN HAPPY.
YOU KNOW ME AS **PUNCHLINE.**

BUT... MY NAME IS **ALEXIS KAYE.**
AND LIKE MANY OF YOU...I AM A **VICTIM** OF THE JOKER.

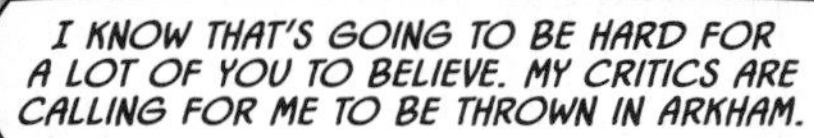

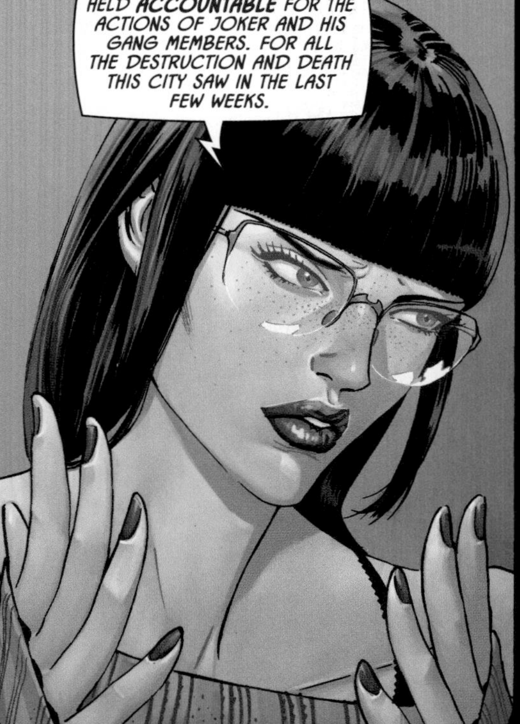
I KNOW THAT'S GOING TO BE HARD FOR A LOT OF YOU TO BELIEVE. MY CRITICS ARE CALLING FOR ME TO BE THROWN IN ARKHAM.
THEY SAY I NEED TO BE HELD **ACCOUNTABLE** FOR THE ACTIONS OF JOKER AND HIS GANG MEMBERS. FOR ALL THE DESTRUCTION AND DEATH THIS CITY SAW IN THE LAST FEW WEEKS.

IF I WERE IN YOUR SHOES, I'D PROBABLY BE SAYING THE SAME THING. I WOULDN'T BUY THE STORIES OF THE STUPID GIRL WHO BELIEVED A MONSTER WHEN HE SAID HE WAS SETTING OUT TO DO GOOD.
I SPENT MONTHS ONLINE TALKING WITH PEOPLE WHO HELD HIM UP AS THIS KIND OF SYMBOL FOR THE PEOPLE WHO SEE THAT THE WORLD IS BROKEN.

AND IT IS, ISN'T IT? I THINK PEOPLE MY AGE SEE IT MOST OF ALL. HOW THE SYSTEMS HAVE BEEN FAILING FOR YEARS. HOW THE SO-CALLED HEROES HAVEN'T DONE ANYTHING TO CHANGE THEM.
I SAW JOKER AS A SYMBOL OF HOW WE NEEDED TO TEAR DOWN THE SYSTEM WE HAD SO WE COULD BUILD SOMETHING NEW. I WANTED TO BELIEVE IN THAT SYMBOL.

AND SO DID HE. HE TWISTED EVERYTHING I SAW IN HIM, FOUND THE EXCUSES FOR WHY HIS OLD ATROCITIES WERE LIES SPREAD BY BATMAN AND THE MEDIA.
HE TOLD ME I COULD HELP HIM BRING HIS MESSAGE TO THE WORLD.

AND MAYBE THAT DOES MAKE ME CRAZY ENOUGH TO THROW ME IN AN ASYLUM. BUT THAT FEELS LIKE LETTING ME OFF TOO EASY.
I BELIEVED IN SOMETHING THAT WASN'T THERE, AND I PUT ON A COSTUME AND BECAME SOMETHING I'M NOT.

AND ONCE I REALIZED THE HORROR UNDERWAY, I WAS TRAPPED, WITH NO WAY OUT.
PEOPLE WERE DYING ALL AROUND ME, AND I SAW THAT THE JOKER WAS EVERY BIT THE MONSTER THE MEDIA CLAIMED HIM TO BE.

I DIDN'T KILL ANYONE, BUT I DIDN'T STOP HIM FROM DOING IT EITHER.
I WAS AN UNWILLING ACCOMPLICE AND WITNESS TO HIS CRIMES. IF THIS CITY DECIDES TO PUT ME AWAY FOREVER...I'LL UNDERSTAND.

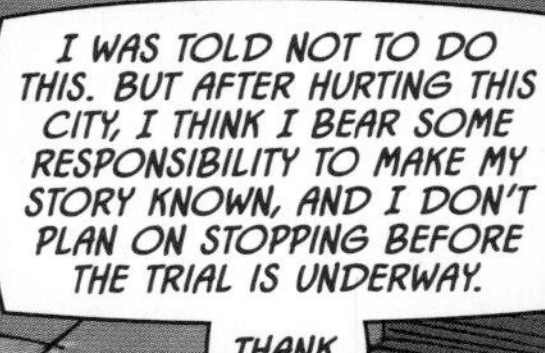

I WAS TOLD NOT TO DO THIS. BUT AFTER HURTING THIS CITY, I THINK I BEAR SOME RESPONSIBILITY TO MAKE MY STORY KNOWN, AND I DON'T PLAN ON STOPPING BEFORE THE TRIAL IS UNDERWAY.
THANK YOU.

SHE'S **VERY** GOOD.
SORRY?
SHE EVEN SAID WHAT SHE'S DOING, RIGHT IN THE VIDEO. THAT'S THE ART OF IT. BRINGING MY MESSAGE TO THE WORLD. *HA!*
THIS TRIAL IS GOING TO BE A ***CIRCUS,*** AND REALLY, THERE'S NO BETTER PLACE FOR A CLOWN.
HEHEHEHEE...
WAIT...
WAIT, YOU'RE NOT...I'M SORRY, YOU SAID YOU WERE A COMEDIAN, SO I'M SURE YOU'RE JUST MAKING A JOKE...
YOU'R
NOT ***H***
ARE YO

NO, NO, NO...
WHAT?
WELL, YOUR BODY WILL BE.
THEY'LL FIND IT DOWN BY ONE OF THE DOCKS IN A DAY OR TWO, ALL BLOATED, WITH THE SKIN BLEACHED JUST RIGHT.
THEY'LL WASTE A FEW WEEKS TRYING TO PROVE IT'S NOT ME. ENOUGH TIME FOR ME TO SET EVERYTHING IN PLACE FOR MY BIG GOODBYE.
I'M PLANNING ON SOME TRAVEL. I THINK A VACATION WILL DO ME SOME GOOD. AS YOU CAN SEE, I COULD USE A LITTLE SUN.
GAK
IT'LL BE NICE. TAKING SOME TIME OFF, LETTING THE CITY MEND ITS BROKEN BONES INTO A BRAND-NEW CONFIGURATION.
YOU SEE, THIS WAS A TEST TO SEE HOW FAR I COULD PUSH THINGS. IT'S TIME FOR US TO ALL START THINKING ABOUT THE FUTURE AND OUR PLACE IN IT.
I JUST BROKE THIS CITY IN WAYS THAT WILL TAKE YEARS TO FULLY RECKON WITH.
IT'S ALL GOING TO CHANGE NOW, AND HE'S GOING TO HAVE TO CHANGE WITH IT.
WHICH IS GOOD. HE WAS STARTING TO GET AWFULLY BORING, DON'T YOU THINK?

I GUESS YOU DON'T THINK ANYMORE, DO YOU, FRIEND?
HEHEHE...
OKAY, THEN...LET'S GET YOU PRETTY.
THERE, THAT'S GOOD, ISN'T IT?
DEAD RINGER
JAMES TYNION IV WRITER
GUILLEM MARCH ARTIST
TOMEU MOREY COLORS
CLAYTON COWLES LETTERS
THAT'S VERY, VERY GOOD.
TO BE CONTINUED

Batman #95 variant cover art by Francesco Mattina

Batman #96 variant cover art by Francesco Mattina

Batman #97 variant cover art by Francesco Mattina

Batman #98 variant cover art by Francesco Mattina

Batman #99 variant cover art by Derrick Chew

Batman #100 variant cover art by Francesco Mattina

Batman #95 character design variant cover art by Jorge Jiménez

Batman #96 character design variant cover art by Jorge Jiménez

Batman #97 character design variant cover art by Jorge Jiménez

Batman #98 character design variant cover art by Jorge Jiménez

Batman #99 character design variant cover art by Jorge Jiménez

Batman #100 character design variant cover art by Jorge Jiménez